ESSEX PARKS

M.W. HANSON

AND

RECORDERS AND MEMBERS

OF THE ESSEX FIELD CLUB

Published by the Essex Field Club

© **ESSEX FIELD CLUB 2004**

c/o School of Health & Biosciences

University of East London

Romford Road, Stratford

London E15 4LZ

www.essexfieldclub.org.uk

Photographs © M.W. Hanson

ISBN 0-905637-17-8

Edited and desk-top publishing by P.R. Harvey

Printed by Jenner (City Print), Tiptree

CONTENTS 1-2

SECTION I: PARKS IN ESSEX 3 - 62

1-2	Introduction
3-7	Parks with particular reference to Essex
8	The current status of a range of Essex Parks
9	The fate of some of the Grand Houses
10-11	The Landscapers of Essex Parks
12	Humphry Repton
13	Park Heritage Status
13	Royal Parks
14-15	Park Boundaries
16	Fencing and Walls in Essex Parks
17-19	Essex Parks on the Map
20	Parks depicted on the Chapman and André Map of 1777
21-23	Belhus, Aveley / Magnificent Thorndon / Hylands, Widford
24-25	Estate Maps in the Essex Records Office
26-27	Four Essex Parks from the Chapman and André Map of 1777
28	Fabulous Wanstead Park
29	The Extent of Essex Parks
30-35	Buildings and other structures within Parks
36-38	Grazing Animals in Parks
39-42	The Great Oaks of Essex Parks and Other Trees
43-45	Oak Pollards in Essex Parks
45-47	Other Notable Specimen Trees in Essex Parks
48-52	The Birds of Essex Parks
53-54	Wood-Pasture and Parks
55	Essex Parks – Location and Access
56-60	Glossary of Park Terms
61-62	Bibliography and References

SECTION II: HYLANDS PARK 63 - 167

63	Introduction – M.W.Hanson
64-69	Hylands – a Brief History. M.W. Hanson
70-76	The Cultivated Landscape – Hylands, its planted trees, shrubs and herbaceous plants. M.W. Hanson
77-78	Geology and Soils. Dr Peter Allen and M.W. Hanson
79-82	Habitats
83-94	Diptera at Hylands Park. Del Smith and M.W. Hanson
95-106	Coleoptera at Hylands Park. Dr Peter Hammond and M.W. Hanson
107-117	Veteran Trees and Saproxylic Invertebrates at Hylands. M.W. Hanson
118-119	Hymenoptera : Aculeata
120-122	Arachnida
123-124	Miscellaneous Invertebrates
125-127	Freshwater Life
128-131	Hylands : Notable Species
132-142	The Higher Plants of Hylands Park. M.W. Hanson
143	Bryophytes
144-145	Lichens John Skinner
146-150	Fungi from Hylands Park. Tony Boniface
151	Amphibians and Reptiles. M.W. Hanson
152-154	The Birds. M.W. Hanson
155-158	Mammals. M.W. Hanson
159-160	Pests and Pathogens. M.W. Hanson
161-166	Conservation Status and Biodiversity. M.W. Hanson
167	Points of Conservation Significance. M.W. Hanson
168-169	Essex Parks – The Eulogy
170	Recording and Registering Essex Parks
171	The Future
171	Acknowledgements
172-175	Index
176-180	B&W illustrations
	8 pages of colour plates

Introduction

The disgrace of Hubert de Burgh in 1239 and his estates, including Hadleigh Park, reverting to the Crown; the disgrace and condemnation of the odious Sir John Gates and the subsequent confiscation of Great and Little Pleshey Parks by the Crown in 1553 and the disgrace and subsequent financial demise of devious MP John Attwood in 1855 causing his loss of Hylands, are typical and indeed part of a continuous thread that weaves its way through the history of parks in Essex. Unlike ancient royal forests, that other great legacy of the wood-pasture tradition that Essex also excels at, parks did not have the continuity of ownership through the Crown and lords of possibly many manors and many commoners with established common rights. Parks being privately owned were subject to the success or failure of their owners (whether politically or financially) and hence lacked the inherent stability conferred by multiple ownership and use. The ebb and flow of emparking and disparking has caused a great fluidity in the very existence of Essex parks. Henry VIII had a mania for creating parks (including a number in Essex) before his death in 1547.The medieval period (Domesday – 1485) saw at least 126 parks in Essex. There is documentary evidence for 160 parks in existence in Essex before 1535. Post-1535 parks bring this total to at least 168 being known in the county. Chapman and André (1777) record some 60 parks (not all medieval in origin and some barely large enough to merit park status). By 1892 only 9 parks stocked with deer remained in Essex, although many others carried sheep and cattle. Many parks by this time had become undistinguished agricultural land.

Essex is an important county in the long history of the creation of parks in England (relatively few parks were created in Wales and Scotland). The history of parks, however, goes back much further than this; they were known in the Middle East some 3,000 years ago. They were known in ancient Assyria, Persia, India and China, as well as Egypt, Greece and Rome. The Persians called their parks 'pairidaeza' whence came our word for paradise (a Paradise Road in Writtle actually leads into Hylands Park!).

In Essex we have the remains of one of the earliest known parks in England – Ongar Great Park – mentioned in an Anglo-Saxon will. Essex also had one of the highest concentrations of medieval parks in England.

Parks were the status symbol of the powerful and wealthy from earliest times. Their uses have changed with the fashions of the day and over the centuries as deer parks ultimately gave way to the landscaped parks of Georgian England.

If one accepts that the average park covered about 250 acres (104 ha.), then parks covered a relatively small area (about 4%) of the land-surface of Essex. But their real significance lay in their ownership. Sooner or later research into any Essex park usually reveals the presence of one or other of the great "movers and shakers" of a particular period in history. I also met the odious Sir John Gates in Havering Park and Fairmead Park, Epping Forest. Lord Richard Rich (rich by name, rich by nature) seems to crop-up regularly as a collector of parks and estates after the Dissolution (1536-40) in Essex. Much of the history of Essex has been played-out against a parkland backdrop. This book is, however, not primarily about wealthy owners and their grand houses. This is covered in many other publications. Rather it is about the evolution of parks from deer park through to landscape park and public park, their everyday uses and lastly, their wildlife.

The book is in two sections. The first gives a brief outline history of parks in Essex and the second takes a look at the history and wildlife of one particular park. – Hylands Park near Chelmsford. This book seeks to put Hylands into some sort of context and to establish its true identity. It also describes how its history has influenced the wildlife found there. It also puts on record the results of a three-year survey undertaken by the Essex Field Club from 2000 to 2003. I hope this will be of great use, not only to current generations of Essex people interested in parks and their history and wildlife, but hopefully also to far-distant generations.

I have to record a debt to three particular authors who have written very scholarly, but readable accounts of parks with references to Essex (see also Bibliography and References): Oliver Rackham and his book Ancient Woodland (1980); Susan Lasdun, The English Park (1992) and Harold Smith, whose History of the Parish of Havering-atte-Bower (1925) contains what must be one of the best researched and detailed accounts of the workings of a royal deer park – Havering Park – from its creation in the 12th century through to its disparking in 1652 and even beyond that. The book also includes the histories of Pyrgo and Bedfords.

Although much of our emparked landscape no longer exists, parks and their owners (and their owners careers!) have had a profound affect on the history and landscape of Essex. The people of Essex should be immensely proud of their parkland heritage.

M.W.Hanson

SECTION I – PARKS IN ESSEX

M.W.HANSON

Parks with particular reference to Essex

The tradition of enclosing an area of land and stocking it with animals was established in England, almost certainly before the Norman Conquest. An Anglo-Saxon will of 1045 refers to "the wood…………..outside the deerhay (deerhage)" at Ongar in the same place where Domesday some forty years later records a park, one of 35 or so (two in Essex) mentioned. Ongar Park at about 1,200 acres (500 ha.) was a sizeable park. It is mentioned as the great park of Aungre in 1243, but had ceased functioning as a working park around 1640. Much of it survived until the 1950s and its destruction is described by Oliver Rackham as one of the "most grievous losses to the south Essex landscape". Part of the boundary bank of the park still survives, as does Ongar Park Wood, part of its coppiced woodland. Much of the land is now farmed and a golf course is currently under construction on part of its site.

The thirteenth and fourteenth centuries were the heyday of the medieval park. Probably well over 2000 were created in Britain, with Essex known to have had around 160 deer parks up to 1535, at least 100 of these being recorded in the period 1230 – 1350. The density works out at approximately one per 10 square miles, one of the densest concentrations in England. Unlike Forests, created mainly by the King (although some nobility – for example the Earls of Richmond and the Bishops of Winchester and Durham – also had forests), a park could be created by anyone wealthy enough to be able to afford one. Most early parks were, however, created by the Crown, nobility or the Church. The establishment of a park required three things – a licence to enclose the ground (particularly in or near a royal forest), a pale (fence) to keep the animals in and the introduction of some deer (sometimes other beasts of the chase). A lodge was also required to oversee the day-to-day working of the park.

Parks would usually be created in a wooded area, although the deer needed grass as well to graze on. Parks usually consisted of existing woodland, pasture and even cultivated land. Heath land is recorded as being emparked at Great Baddow in 1247. There are also mentions of 'launds' - grassy plains being created in parks by grubbing-out existing woodland.

Larger parks were created early on in this period. It is assumed that it was easier then, particularly for the Crown, to gather together larger parcels of land. Some of these large early parks may have had red deer, as well as fallow. Large early parks include Ongar (1,200 acres) mentioned in 1045, Rayleigh (800 – 1,000 acres) mentioned in 1086, and Havering (1,300 acres) mentioned in 1157. Havering and Rayleigh were royal parks (of at least 18 in Essex). Havering remained in royal ownership until disparked. Some of the other royal parks were only briefly held by the Crown.

There are many records of royal grants of deer to start parks in Essex. Henry III gave twenty does to Hugo de Neville to stock his park at Great Hallingbury in 1221. Havering Park (near to what is now Collier Row) is first mentioned in 1157. As a royal park, Havering supplied deer for the King's table for feasts and as gifts in the form of venison and also live animals to start other deer parks. Domestic stock also grazed the park. It was also a significant supplier of timber. In many parks pollard trees and coppiced woodland – the latter fenced off (compartmented) from browsing livestock – provided firewood and wood for other uses. In Havering, timber from the park was used in building works at the Tower of London; in 1278 100 oaks were ordered (with 120 to come from

Hadleigh Park as well). In 1217 oaks had been ordered for works at the old St Paul's Cathedral. Other, lesser uses, of oak from Havering Park included that for construction or repairs to various other buildings, including the King's houses at Havering in the early 13th century and the construction of a chapel at Hornchurch in 1313. In 1220 Oak from Havering was given to make two refectory tables at Barking Abbey. Oak is also recorded for laths and shingles. Much dead wood was given as firewood. Later, in 1609, timber from Havering is recorded as being used for repairs to the 'clapgate, deerleape, water-gate and lodges'. In 1652, when Havering was finally disparked, the big trees remaining were marked for the use of the Navy.

Early parks, such as Hadleigh, may have been considered to be an integral part of a much larger estate. Hadleigh Castle (built outside the park) in the 13th century was surrounded by a demesne farm, with arable, meadow and pasture, a vineyard, coppiced woodland, a coastal fishery and a water-mill, as well as the deer park. It was only later that deer parks came to be seen in isolation, in their own right, not just as part of a utilitarian enterprise, but as great symbols of the power, status and wealth of their owners (particularly as, from the fourteenth century onwards, more and more grand houses came to be built within the confines of the park pale). The role of parks began to change from being a utilitarian supplier of venison to the setting for a splendid mansion.

During the Dissolution, the confiscation of monastic estates and their subsequent re-distribution amongst the faithful courtiers of Henry VIII caused probably a third of England to change ownership. The vast land holdings of Lord Richard Rich made it easy for him to enlarge parks, create new parks, or consolidate his ownership of existing medieval parks, as he did at his seat of Leez Priory near Littley Green. His three parks clustered around Leez Priory alone totalled almost 1,500 acres (625 ha.).

Henry VIII confiscated numerous parks from the church, as well as creating new ones. In south-west Essex alone, he appropriated Copped Hall and created new parks at Fairmead in Epping Forest, Waltham and Nazeing. Elizabeth I is said to have inherited at least 180 royal parks. Perhaps the most important and enduring legacy of Henry VIII is Queen Elizabeth's Hunting Lodge (which was actually neither Queen Elizabeth's nor a Hunting Lodge) built around 1542 – 43 as a Great Standing when Henry emparked Fairmead in Epping Forest. Parokes, a complex series of internal enclosures, were also constructed at Fairmead at this time. They were probably intended to control the numbers of deer being entered for a stage-managed Tudor ritual hunt.

The practice of siting mansions in parks also led to gardens being created around the house and as the fashion of the time led to a change of emphasis from a utilitarian enterprise producing venison, to visual amenity, the actual landscape of parks began to change. The early gardens, with their parterres, knot gardens and topiary, in some cases came to be extended into the park, with avenues of trees and later elaborate formal plantings of trees. One of the earliest avenues of trees axial to a house was planted at New Hall, Boreham, in 1624 by John Tradescant, Keeper of His Majesty's Gardens to Charles I. The avenue, a mile long of 1,000 lime trees in four rows, each of 250 trees some 3ft in diameter, were felled and sold to a Chelmsford timber merchant in 1800. A partial replacement avenue has been planted.

It is thought that between 1570 and 1620, more new country houses were built in parts of England than at any other period of time. In Essex, the huge Jacobean 'palace' of Audley End near Saffron Walden was created between 1605 and 1614 by Thomas Howard, grandson of Sir Thomas Audley, who had acquired the Benedictine Walden Abbey (founded c.1140) and park in 1538. Sir Thomas Audley adapted the Abbey for domestic use, but his grandson Thomas Howard subsequently demolished this building in its entirety and set about creating what became the largest Jacobean 'prodigy' house ever built. The house was centred around what had been the cloister of the old abbey, with a vast courtyard (the outer court). As ever, the fortunes of the house and park waxed and waned with the fortunes of the owner. Thomas Howard was convicted of embezzlement and after a brief imprisonment in the Tower, retired in disgrace to Audley End.

Parks and their great houses were often a drain on the resources of their owners and by 1609, even the number of royal parks had dwindled to around a hundred. Audley End, however, did become a later royal holding (by Charles II from 1668 – 88), but this royal ownership was relatively brief, and the house reverted back to the Earls of Suffolk in 1701. The vast mansion was eventually to prove too much of a burden to subsequent owners and it was eventually much reduced in size and the house we see today is less than half of the former Jacobean mansion.

The civil war brought park-making to an abrupt standstill – parks were seen to be a powerful royalist symbol (the licence to empark was at the behest of the Crown). Royal parks were confiscated and sold to fund the unpaid wages of parliamentarian soldiers. Other parks were raided for their timber and deer. In 1643 there was a complaint "….that divers unruly persons without any authority, do daily enter into the Park of Havering ……..and there cut, destroy and root up the trees growing in the said park, and also pull down the pales and inclosures thereof;……it……..would be the utter destruction of the park and deer therein". Havering eventually became one of the many royal parks disparked and sold during the Commonwealth in 1652.

Sir Josiah Child, Chairman of the East India Company, purchased the old Wanstead House and Park in 1667 and he spent a fortune on planting the park. In 1683 the diarist, John Evelyn, visited Wanstead "…..to see Sir Josiah Child's prodigious cost in planting walnut trees about his seate ………in Epping Forest". Child also planted lime avenues and sweet chestnut in complex quincunx formations, some trees of which survive to this day, including some huge sweet chestnuts. In 1715 the old Wanstead House was demolished and in its place one of the finest and most splendid - but short-lived - examples of Palladian architecture ever seen in England, to a design by Colen Campbell, took its place.

The creation of artificial water features (ie not for utilitarian fish or stock ponds), but for visual pleasure, was a concept readily taken-up by park owners and re-invented by the 18th century landscapers. Artificial lakes became a feature of many parks, including Audley End, Wanstead and later, Hylands.

A very complex landscaping plan for Thorndon Park was drawn-up by the landscaper Bourginion and the eighth Lord Petre. Presumably because of its vast scale, it was never completed and ultimately the ninth Lord Petre commissioned the famous Lancelot 'Capability' Brown in 1778 to draw-up plans for the park centred on the new James Paine mansion of 1764 – 70. This obliterated much of the Bourginion work. The 1777 Chapman and Andre map shows Thorndon Park as a separate entity from the neighbouring Childerditch (and little Warley) Common. In a 1774 survey Childerditch Common had listed for it 2,080 oak pollards and 1,323 hornbeam trees. By 1805 the Henry Clayton estate map shows this common to have been incorporated into the new park (now Thorndon Park North). Subsequently many of the old pollards were destroyed and plantations created in their place. Today one sees just the odd, old pollard amongst even more recent plantations of Beech, Larch, Scots Pine, Sweet Chestnut and Oak.

Brown had earlier landscaped Audley End in 1762 under the watchful eye of Sir John Griffin Griffin (later Lord Howard de Walden). Under Brown much of the formal Jacobean plantings were swept away (or disguised) and a more open, naturalistic park was created. Brown also contrived a park within a park as a private area for the family, forming this from the old deer park. He also dammed the River Cam to create a sizeable lake and created a great ha-ha with a walk (to keep out the deer). The architect Robert Adam designed a number of buildings in the park, including temples in the Ionic and Corinthian orders, a Palladian bridge, an obelisk and a gateway, all constructed between 1763 and 1791.

Mock temples and statuary appeared in many parks in the 18th century, as well as romantic ruins - attempts by owners to emulate the classical buildings and ruins seen in great paintings and on their Grand Tours to the continent - although Capability Brown typically was not a great user of such props in his schemes. An 18th century temple (rotunda) and obelisk can still be seen at Warlies Park and a grotto and 'temple' at Wanstead still survive.

The late 18th and early 19th century saw many parks in Essex landscaped by Humphry Repton. He is thought to have worked on, or been associated in some way with, over 30 properties in Essex. His more noteworthy commissions, included Claybury Hall (Chigwell), Hill Hall (Theydon Mount), Hylands (Chelmsford), Rivenhall Place (Rivenhall), Stansted Hall (Stansted Mountfitchet) and Wanstead House (Wanstead). There was a movement away from the formal to a more naturalistic appearance of parks, even some gardens disappeared from around the house – the park being brought right up to the walls of the house in some of Brown's schemes.

It is against this background that Hylands makes its late and rather unobtrusive debut in about 1730, the house being constructed in red brick in the Queen Anne style between 1728 and 1730. The house was built on an eminence - hence Hylands (but strangely not the highest point) - by John Comyns, a prominent lawyer, Member of Parliament and later, Chief Baron of the Exchequer.

The Victorian period seems to have had little impact on Essex parks (although some, like Hylands, were greatly enlarged at this time), with the exception of the cultivated environment – Kitchen Gardens and the gardens around the house appear to have been the focus of Victorian horticultural endeavour. There seems to be no Victorian equivalent of Capability Brown or Humphry Repton who worked extensively in Essex. One characteristic tree of this period though, is the Wellingtonia (introduced 1853). A 'must have' fashion tree, it occurs in parks all over Essex as singletons, in small groups, avenues (Havering Park) and bulk-planted at Stansted Hall. Other (largely) Victorian plantings include Deodar (introduced 1831) and Californian Redwood (introduced 1843). It remains to be seen what impact the Wellingtonia will have on the visual quality of earlier landscapes. Havering Park, with at least 63 Wellingtonias in and around the Avenue, is said to have one of the largest concentrations of this species in England. Some parks appear to have acquired plantations of conifers during this period.

The 20th century was not good for our parks. Our cavalier (or should I say roundhead) attitude to our parkland heritage at these times, although no worse than that of previous generations, is probably best summed-up by the destruction of the Anglo-Saxon Ongar Great Park in the 1950s. Many of our parks have been obliterated by modern farming and a number of the old mansions burnt or demolished, although a surprising number still survive. A number of parks have had railways and roads driven through them. Others have had gravel extracted or become golf courses. Those near London have been particularly prone to urban development. The long history of Copped Hall near Epping, summarised below, neatly illustrates the broad history of parks in Essex.

Initially Copped Hall may have been only a small park. Henry II (1154 – 89) had granted land of two acres for a house and garden. The park was subsequently enlarged in 1231 and 1295, on the latter occasion by just 15 acres. By 1303 the park was said to cover 60 acres. In 1350 Copped Hall was conveyed to the Abbots of Waltham, who in 1374 were granted a licence to enlarge Copped Hall Park and Harolds Park (in nearby Nazeing) by 120 acres. Waltham Abbey held Copped Hall until the dissolution and eventually ownership fell to Elizabeth I. In 1562 a commission was set-up by the Queen to view "what spoil, waste or destruction hath been made of any of our timber, trees, woods or underwoods………and what pales, rails and posts or gates………hath been lately pulled down, spoiled, defaced or carried away……" in the park.

The lessee (Sir Thomas Cornwallis) was found to have felled much timber, but used it for building a wash-house and for making furniture, including sixteen bedsteads and two great tables. By this time the medieval Copped Hall was in a ruinous state and a later owner (Thomas Heneage) built a new Copped Hall on the site in 1568, possibly incorporating some of the medieval building. The Tudor Copped Hall was demolished in the 1750s and a new Georgian hall erected some distance away by the owner, John Conyers, being completed about 1758. The park was landscaped by Capability Brown, probably in the 1750s. In the late 19th century, very elaborate Italianate gardens were created around the house.

The 18th century Copped Hall is now just a shell, but currently undergoing restoration. The house was gutted by fire in 1917. Some of the old coppiced woodland shown on the Chapman and Andre map of 1777 has been grubbed-up and some coniferised. The old stable block and dairy are converted to domestic dwellings. The M25 has neatly divided the park into two sections. The park, along with Warlies, has also become part of the buffer lands around Epping Forest. Warlies and Copped Hall (and Hylands) have all had what were formerly arable fields returned to pasture or meadow grassland.

Perhaps the last word should go to the park of Easton Lodge, near Dunmow. The house was said to have been built on the site of the park lodge. In the dark days of the second world war, the park of 700 acres was virtually completely obliterated by the construction of an American bomber base, with the loss of many hundreds of trees.

The current status of a range of Essex Parks

Farmed (arable) Blake Hall, Absol, Crondon (part), Gosfield, Felix Hall, Hatfield, Stansted Hall (part), Barrington Hall (part), Hallingbury Place (part), Ongar, Havering, Pleshey Great, Pleshey Little, Littley, Writtle (plus many others)

Coniferised (partly) Copped Hall, Chalkney Wood, Thorndon, Weald, Marks Hall

Golf Course Belhus, Audley End, Ongar, Wanstead, Thorndon, Braxted, Crondon, Gidea (all partly)

Developed (partly) Gaynes (Upminster), Wanstead, Moulsham Hall, Highams, Claybury (now Repton Park and formerly the hospital), Havering, Wivenhoe Park (Essex University), Hare Hall, Hargrave, Gidea

Gravel Extraction St Osyth (partly)

Public Park (including Country Park) Thorndon (N & S), Weald, Hylands, Wanstead, Danbury, Bedfords, West Ham, Norsey Wood, Chalkney Wood, Havering

Roads built through Belhus (M25), Copped Hall (M25), Stansted Hall (M11), Hylands (London Road, now A414 and Writtle by-pass A414)

Railways constructed in New Hall, Mistley, Stansted Hall, Hare Hall

Still Privately Owned Rivenhall, St Osyth, Quendon, Braxted, Gaynes Park (Theydon)

Epping Forest Buffer Lands Warlies, Copped Hall (both Corporation of London)

Aldersbrook is now a cemetery and crematorium. Gilwell is now a Boy Scout camp site, as is Skreens at Roxwell (in part)

The fate of some of the grand houses

BURNT	DEMOLISHED	SURVIVORS (selection of)	CONVERTED (to flats)
Weald Hall	Bedfords	Ingatestone Hall	Hill Hall
Copped Hall*	Wanstead House	New Hall (in part)	Thorndon Hall
Hill Hall	Hallingbury Place	Hylands	Hassobury
Felix Hall	Dagnams	Rochetts	Elsenham Hall
Mark Hall	Weald Hall	Audley End (much reduced)	
Thorndon Hall	Moor Hall	Spains Hall	**SCHOOLS**
Shortgrove Hall	Albyns	Blake Hall	
	Belhus	Claybury Hall	Hare Hall
	Gosfield Place	Highams	Brizes
	Marks Hall	Langleys	New Hall
		Riffhams	Highams
		St Osyth's Priory (in part)	
		Barrington Hall	**RESIDENTIAL HOMES**
		Wivenhoe House	
		Rivenhall Place	Copford Place
		Boreham House	Gosfield Hall
		Braxted	Hargrave House
		Terling Place	
		Warlies	**HOTELS**
		Quendon	
			Wivenhoe House
*Remaining shell currently being restored			DownHall

The landscapers of Essex parks

John Tradescant the Elder (c.1570 – 1638)

New Hall, Boreham (1624)

George London (d.1713/14)

Wanstead Park, Wanstead (1713)

Charles Bridgeman (d.1738)

Langleys, Great Waltham (1718/1719)
Bower House, Romford (1729)
Down Hall, Hatfield Broad Oak (1720)

Adam Holt (1691? – 1750)

Wanstead Park, Wanstead (1715)?
Castle Hedingham (1726)
Coopersale House, Epping (1738)

Bourginion & the 8th Lord Petre (1713 – 1742)

Thorndon, Brentwood (1733)

Lancelot Brown (1716 – 1783)

Audley End, Saffron Walden (1762)
Belhus, Aveley (1753)
Copped Hall, Epping (c.1750s?)
Hallingbury Place, Great Hallingbury (1758 and 1778)
Navestock Hall, Ongar (1763)
Shortgrove, Saffron Walden (1758)
Thorndon, Brentwood (1766 – 1772)

Richard Woods (1716 – 1793)

Audley End, Saffron Walden (1780)
Boreham House, Boreham (1771 – 1772)
Brizes, Kelvedon Hatch (1788)

Copford Hall, Colchester (1784)
Great Myles, Kelvedon Hatch (1771 and 1787)
Hare Hall, Romford (1768/69)
Hatfield Priory, Hatfield Peverel (1765)
Marks Hall, Coggeshall (1779)?
New Hall, Boreham (1767 and 1775/76)
Stanway, Colchester (1792)
Wivenhoe Park, Wivenhoe (1765, 1776 – 1780)

Humphry Repton (1752 – 1818)

Claybury Hall, Chigwell (1791)
Dagnams, Harold Hill (c.1802)
Felix Hall, Kelvedon (c.1794)
Gosfield Place, Halstead (c.1811)
Hallingbury Place, Great Hallingbury (before 1803)
Highams, Woodford (1793)
Hill Hall, Theydon Mount (1791)
Hylands, Widford (after 1797)
Langleys, Great Waltham (c.1803)
Mark Hall, Latton (from 1789)
Moor Hall, Harlow (1808)
Rivenhall Place, Rivenhall (1789)
Spains Hall, Finchingfield (1807)
Stansted Hall, Stansted Mountfitchet (1791)
Suttons, Stapleford Tawney (before 1803)
Wanstead Park, Wanstead (1813)
Woodford Hall, Woodford (1801)

William Sawrey Gilpin (1762 – 1843)

Audley End, Saffron Walden (probably c.1800)

Owner/Landscaper

Richard Morgan

Warlies (1720 – 1740)

Humphry Repton

Humphry Repton, the landscape gardener, was born in Bury St Edmunds in 1752 and educated at Norwich Grammar School. He married Mary Clarke in 1773. John Adey Repton, their second child, was born in 1775 and was later to work with his father on many of his projects.

Around 1786, after losing money in a second business venture, he moved to Hare Street, near Romford from where, in 1788, he started his career as a landscape gardener, his first commission being Catton Hall in Norfolk.

In Essex he is thought to have been associated with over 30 properties, amongst his most notable being Claybury, Gosfield Place, Highams, Hylands, Rivenhall Place, Stansted Hall and Wanstead.

Famous for his Red Books with before-and-after watercolour scenes of his suggested improvements, the Red Book for Hylands is unfortunately lost (last seen in 1839), but at least seven related to Essex properties are known to survive. The "Red Book" for Wanstead was 'discovered' in 2002 when it came-up for sale at a provincial auction house. Mis-described in the catalogue and estimated at £1,000 - £2,000, it eventually sold for £58,000 (see page 180).

The early 1790s were the peak period for Repton's landscaping work. He also published a number of books on the subject of landscaping. In 1811 he was seriously injured in a carriage accident, which severely affected his ability to work. However, he still managed to produce his Red Book for Wanstead in 1813. In 1815 he worked on Riffhams at Danbury with his son John Adey (1775 – 1860). John Adey eventually retired to Springfield, Chelmsford (designing Trinity Church in 1843). Another son, George Stanley Repton, also an architect, is famous for collaborating with his father and brother on plans for the Royal Pavillion at Brighton and also for 'running-off' and marrying the daughter of Lord Eldon.

Humphry died in 1818 at Hare Street and was buried at Aylsham, Norfolk

HUMPHRY REPTON 1752 - 1818

Park Heritage Status

The following is a selected list of parks from the English Heritage – Register of Parks and Gardens of Historic Interest Part 15, Essex published in 1987 with later revisions:

Audley End	I	New Hall	II
Blake Hall	II	Quendon	II
Boreham House	II	St Osyth	II
Braxted	II*	Spains Hall	II*
Copped Hall	II*	Thorndon	II*
Hylands	II*	Weald Park	II
Langleys	II	Wivenhoe	II

For a very few, such as Audley End, Hylands, Thorndon and Weald, the park is still a recognisable entity with a wood-pasture landscape. For others, such as Boreham, the house now sits in a much reduced parkland setting with the remainder of the park being farmed. Virtually nothing remains of the park of New Hall. I suspect the list needs updating with amendments and additions.

Royal Parks

The parks listed below have at some stage been royal parks, some – such as Havering, for their entire existence (1157 – 1652) – others, such as Audley End only briefly (1668 – 1701). Fairmead may have existed for as little as thirteen years before disparking, Waltham lasted a mere 6 years from 1542 – 1548.

Audley End	Eastwood	Langham	Rayleigh
Clavering	Fairmead	Nazeing	Rochford
Copped Hall	Hadleigh	New Hall	Thundersley
Crondon	Hatfield	Pyrgo	Waltham
	Havering		Wanstead

Park Boundaries

The usual park boundary up to the late 18th century was the park pale, a fence of cleft oak pales supported by a framework of posts, rails and struts. The pales were pointed at the base, this end being driven into the ground. The pale was then nailed or otherwise fixed to the top rail to prevent it from being moved. The pales were alternately long and short, presumably to help reduce costs. The long pales could be re-cut at the base and used again as short pales.

It seems to have been part of the manorial service that "….men of the same manor as others of the neighbourhood outside ought to renew and repair that paling as often as need be" (Havering Park, 1306 – 7). The customal of Hatfield Broad Oak says much the same thing - in 1328, a particular tenant was required to "….make and keep 32 perches of pale round the park ….and shall have the old timber of the said pale when it is not worth putting back …..".

In all, 49 tenants had to maintain 151 perches of pale and 129 perches of hedge around Hatfield Park, a total of almost a mile. It seems, however, that by the late 14th century the service at Hatfield was commuted to a fine and the pale was inspected and a contractor hired to undertake the actual work. In 1444 25 perches of new fence were required and 48 perches of old fence repaired. The pales were to be re-pointed. The cost was calculated at 4d per perch for new fence and 2d per perch for old.

Smith records several mentions of the park pale being put into repair in Havering Park. By 1531 Havering employed a Keeper of the Pale and also a paler (palystere) to maintain the fence around the 1300 acre park.

In 1594 accounts for the preparation of a visit by Queen Elizabeth to Havering include several entries for paling and rails around the palace and garden:

	£	s	d
two hundred of cleft pale at 6 shillings the hundred		12	0
for half a load of rayles		9	0
five hundred cleft pale at 6s ye c	1	10	0
20 posts at 10d a post		16	8

In 1624 a warrant for £230 was issued for the repair of Havering Park pale. During the Civil War it was recorded that the pale at Havering was pulled down "by divers unruly persons".

The 60-odd parks shown on Chapman and Andre (1777) are virtually all shown with a pale, exceptions include Audley End and a handful of others (Shortgrove, Mark Hall, Moulsham Hall and Wardens Hall, Willingale Spain). Audley End was walled and the others were possibly just hedged or fenced, rather than paled.

An account of the construction of the King's 'newe parke' adjacent to the recently dissolved Waltham Abbey in 1542, mentions the inclosing and paling of the park – the pales, posts and rails coming from Cheton Wood. Part of the boundary of Waltham Park may also have been partly hedged, since the 'gatherying of quickesetts for the dyche by the parke syde' is also mentioned. This is possibly a reference to that part of the park that runs by Cobbins Brook which, because of the meandering and bank erosion, would probably have been difficult to pale. The Hylands Park of 1777 was completely surrounded by a pale, as was the enlarged park of 1838 when much of the oak paling was renewed.

Park walls, presumably because of the expense and time involved in construction, are a rarity. Audley End's wall was extant in 1676, but was reported to be "falling Downe in many places" in 1701. Braxted's wall at 3.4 miles long completely surrounds the park and was built 1825 – 31 in soft red brick. This too had collapsed in places, but like Audley End, is now in a good state of repair with sections replaced and earlier piers built to hold-up the leaning wall. Hylands wall, almost a mile long, was originally built c.1841 by John Attwood along the boundary of the London Road, probably for privacy reasons, rather than to retain livestock. This wall was re-built in the 1930s within the boundary of the park when the London Road was dualled. A circa 180ft section of the southern end of this wall collapsed in 2002 (reinstated in 2003). Shortgrove has a later low brick-capped flint wall.

In many cases the pale stood on top of a bank and ditch, often good evidence where the park is now gone. The Saxon Ongar Great Park, now a scheduled monument, has an imposingly massive ditch and bank, the bank in places being four to five feet or more high. Braxted has a curious boundary in that part of the length of the north wall is followed by a deep ditch, the far side topped with hornbeam stools that have laterally extended branches to form a barrier. The ditch is six or seven feet deep in places (at one point I believe nearer ten). The Braxted Park of 1831 was much enlarged in the west and east from the park shown on the Chapman and Andre map of 1777.

Weald Park was fenced with a cleft-oak pale as late as 1933 (supplied by Brace of High Ongar), although it was apparently largely destroyed in World War II.

Fencing and walls in Essex Parks

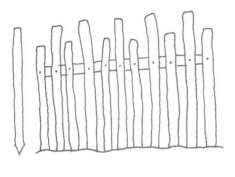

Medieval Park Pale

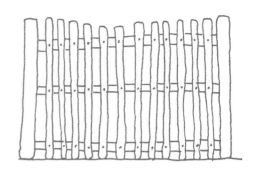

Section of Pale, Copped Hall 1988

Northern wall and ditch - Braxted Park 2003

Park fencing of the type used at Langleys and Rivenhall 2003

Park Pale at Hylands c.1804 from Peacock's "Polite Repository"

Essex Parks on the Map

Prior to the reign of Elizabeth I (1558 – 1603) there were no local estate maps showing the ownerships of an area of land. Land ownership was (if at all!) confirmed by a written description with boundaries marked at certain points on a prominent feature, such as a tree with sometimes a physical boundary marker being placed between manors or parishes. Fences, hedges, brooks, rivers, woods, commons, roads, all served as boundaries. Sometimes the boundary was confirmed by perambulation; 'beating the bounds' was an annual event in some parishes.

Parks were different, in that the boundary was, in most cases, strictly defined by a boundary bank topped by a pale and sometimes a hedge and so there could be little argument (once the park was established) as to who owned what. Parks, unlike the open-bounded Forest, could hardly be subject to any illegal enclosure without someone noticing.

Possibly stimulated by the vast changes in land ownership caused by the Dissolution of the monasteries in 1536 – 1540, when up to a third of England is thought to have changed hands, there may have been a real need for the new land-owners to have some idea of the extent of their often dispersed land-holdings. It must have been very difficult for the land agents or bailiffs when confronted by, for example, the vast new estates of an owner – such as Rich of Leez Priory – to know exactly where the boundaries lay. Without knowing your property's extent, it would be impossible to effectively manage or value it for a tenancy.

The estate map would also help to solve the problem of the absentee landlord in dealing with something that arose on a far-away estate. A map would also define (more than the written word could) and confirm a boundary – important, for example, in a dispute between tenants.

The second half of the sixteenth century saw the rise of the land surveyor and the estate map. One of the earliest estate maps in the Essex Record Office is a plan of Ingatestone Hall and grounds dated 1566. Perhaps the most famous of the early Essex surveyors were the Walkers, father and son and both called John, of Hanningfield, who produced accurate yet very attractive maps from 1586 onwards. A set of Walker maps of East and West Hanningfield of 1615 has in the introductory text "……..and also you shall find in the said plates, the parish churches with the parsonages and glebe lands, the park impaled, the demesne lands and mansion houses, with the freehold and copyhold lands and houses set forth in their true places and proportions and also all the gates, stiles, bars, rails, ponds, rivers, brooks, bridges, highways, lanes and driftways". As is usual, the park was surveyed with the rest of the estate.

An earlier map of c.1595 (surveyor unknown) shows an oblique "aerial" view of land north of Waltham Abbey showing Copped Hall, Harold's and Waltham Parks. Despite Waltham Park being disparked in 1548 (it only existed for 6 years from 1542), it is still depicted at this late date being surrounded by a park pale. However, the western half of the park is shown with a hedged internal landscape – a possible result of partial disparking. The original of this map is in Hatfield House, Hertfordshire.

The year of 1598 saw the making of the Earls Colne map by Israel Amyce (Ames) who was one of the agents appointed to administer the estates of Edward de Vere, the 17th Earl of Oxford, and it was from this map that we learn that the de Veres "bredd and mayntayned Wyelde Swyne" in Chalkney Wood. Such large and at times destructive animals were imparked, breaking out through a weakness in the pale every now and then to cause damage to farms in the vicinity. This survey was done with great accuracy; the outline of the Chalkney Wood of 1598 is shown to be identical with that of modern Ordnance Survey Maps.

A slightly later, and much less accurate map of the Keepers Walks in Epping Forest c.1630 (but possibly earlier and again surveyor unknown), shows twelve parks in south-west Essex (notably Warlies is not shown):

Bedfords	Havering	Pyrgo
Copped Hall	Latton	Waltham
Gaynes (Theydon)	Nelmes	Wanstead
Harold's	Ongar (Vnger)	Wintry

The parks are shown in stylised form with no accurate detail (Bedfords appears to be depicted without a pale). Waltham Park is depicted without being named, but it does show Havering Park in the last years of its existence, before being disparked in 1652. The original of this map is in the Public Record Office.

Estate maps, although utilitarian in purpose, were often decorated with an elaborate cartouche and polar indicator, particularly in the 18th century, to delight the eye of those who had commissioned them. Armorial bearings were sometimes incorporated into the maps – the surveyor Thomas Browne (1702 – 80) was better known as a herald, becoming Garter King of Arms in 1774. Browne surveyed Lord Waldegrave's estate at Navestock in 1726. On the map he shows decoys and deer in the park and also incorporated the Waldegrave Arms. Many surveyors appear to have had other jobs – many were teachers and farmers doing land surveying as a sideline – perhaps as and when the weather or farming calendar permitted.

The 18th and early 19th century was the golden age of the land surveyor – some outstanding maps of Essex parks were made during this period – John Rocque - Wanstead (1735); Edward John Eyre – St Osyth's (1762); John Mackoun – Barrington Hall (1766); Peter Bernard Scalé – Mistley Hall (1788) and Henry Clayton – Thorndon (1805) amongst many. Rocque and Scalé, both Huguenots, bring us to John Chapman and Peter André – the latter also a Huguenot. Scalé lived for a time at Warley. His sister Mary Ann married John Rocque and carried-on the business after her husband's death in 1763. It was probably she who solicited subscriptions for a county map of Essex – resulting in what is one of the finest pieces of 18th (or indeed any) century cartography – the Chapman and André map surveyed 1772 – 74 and published in 1777. John Chapman of Dalham, Suffolk, was the surveyor.

The map of 26 engraved sheets at a scale of 2 inches to a mile, is an astonishing piece of work – bearing direct comparison with the modern Ordnance Survey. It is one of the most important references for a landscape historian working on Essex today. It accurately defines saltings, marsh, fens, heaths, commons, village greens, tyes, ancient royal forests, coppiced woodlands and from the point of view of this publication – parks.

Firstly it names the then owner of the park (some of these were subscribers to the map). The park boundary is also indicated, most parks are shown with a pale, Audley End is shown with its wall (Braxted's wall did not happen until 1825). Others are shown without pale or wall. Possibly they were hedged or fenced (like Langleys and Rivenhall today). The mansion itself and gardens are also shown (not very accurately at this scale). Lesser features, such as carriage turn-arounds are also shown (New Hall). Landscape features, such as lakes and avenues of trees (Wanstead and many others) are often depicted; occasionally vistas (Easton) are also indicated. Specimen pollard and standard trees are shown (often stylised and sometimes inaccurately, as in Mistley Park), within the park.

In Writtle (now disparked) an immense tree appears to be shown – probably an old pollard oak. Coppiced Woodland appears in some parks (Copped Hall, Barrington Hall). In others belts of trees (planted on the park boundary) seem to be indicated (Navestock, Mistley). Buildings other than the mansion are also depicted – farms (Thorndon), rarely churches (Faulkbourne) and a windmill (Mistley). Lodges also seem to be rare at this time, but what is presumably an ancient lodge is shown in the middle of Weald Park. This park is also shown with what is presumably the Belvedere (slightly out of position). Other landscape 'props' shown on the map include the rotunda and obelisk at Warlies.

Very occasionally the site of disparked parks is shown. Examples include Havering (gone by 1652), Hadleigh (gone by 1550) and the second park at St Osyth (shown as simply "The Park" east of the existing park). Writtle Park is shown with some sort of paled internal enclosure, possibly to separate livestock. Usefully the key sheet depicts the sixty-odd parks then found in Essex on the one sheet, but obviously at a much smaller scale.

Some individual parks shown are quite superb – Thorndon comes to mind with its yet to be enclosed Childerditch Common and the park and avenues running from West Horndon to Brentwood, its almost 1,000 acres being the largest park in Essex at that time. Lord Petre notably subscribed to four sets of the map!

Other pre-Ordnance Survey County Maps showing parks include Christopher Saxton (1576), John Norden (1594), Joannes Blaeu (1645) and John Oliver (1696).

Parks depicted on the Chapman and André Map of Essex 1777

The following parks are taken from the main map (not the Key Sheet). The main map also sometimes shows the location of long-gone parks – examples include Havering, St Osyth (2), Hatfield, Hadleigh (Hadley) and Crondon (Cranham). The list also includes some smaller parks.

Abury Hatch	Debden	Lexden	Rolls
Albyns	Donyland (East)	Luxborough	St Osyth (1)
Aldersbrook	Donyland (West)	Lyston	Shortgrove
Audley End	Down Hall	Mark Hall	Skreens
Barrington Hall	Easton Lodge	Marks	Terling
Baythorne	Faulkbourne	Marks Hall	Thorndon
Bedfords	Felix Hall	Mistley	Upper House
Belhus	Gidea	Moulsham Hall	Valence
Bifrons	Gilwell	Myles's	Valentines
Boreham	Gosfield	Navestock Hall	Waltons
Bower Hall	Hackton Hill	New Hall	Wanstead
Braxted	Hallingbury	Oldfield Grange	Wardens Hall
Brittons	Highams	Parsloes	Warlies
Copped Hall	Hill Hall	Pyrgo	Weald
Coptfold Hall	Hylands	Quendon	West Ham
Dagnam	Kelvedon Hall	Ray House	Wivenhoe
Danbury	Langleys	Rivenhall	Writtle

Belhus, Aveley

A sixteenth century house, remodelled in the eighteenth century. The park was established in 1618.

Lancelot Brown worked on the park in 1753. Note how the park goes right up to the house. The house was demolished in 1957 and the M25 now goes through what was the eastern edge of the park. Some of the land, referred to now as Belhus Chase, has been heavily planted by the Woodland Trust (since 1998). It was returning from a ball at Belhus in 1811 that Humphry Repton sustained his debilitating injury in a carriage accident. (Engraving c.1832, Map 1777).

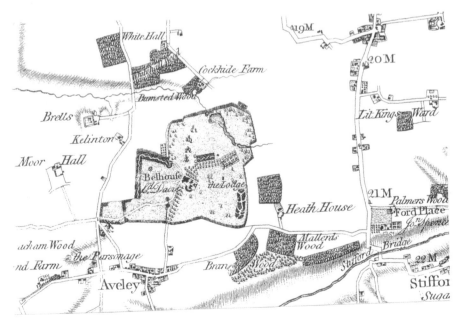

BELHUS PARK AND HOUSE, NEAR AVELEY c.1777

Magnificent Thorndon

The engraving shows the James Paine mansion of 1764 – 70. The map shows the park as it was in 1772 – 4 not long after landscaping by Capability Brown. The original 300 acre park of 1414 is now (partly) Thorndon Park South, the old hall being demolished when the new was built. 1734 – 1742 Thorndon was famed for the cultivation in huge hot-houses of exotic fruits, such as Pineapple, Banana, Guava and Papaya under the guidance of the 8th Lord Petre.

By 1805 the park had incorporated Childerditch Common, now Thorndon Park North. Sadly most of its 2,000 oak pollards were destroyed. Thorndon at this time was said to cover 1,077 acres, farming mainly deer and sheep. (Engraving c.1831, map 1777).

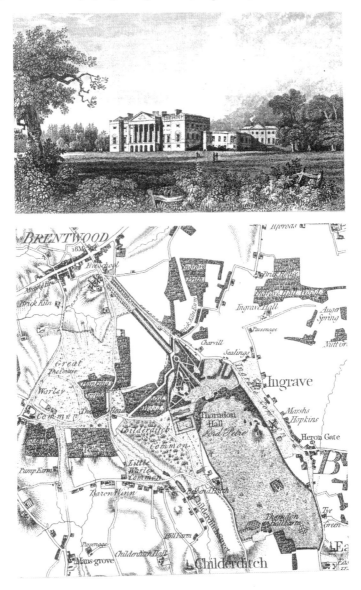

THORNDON NEAR BRENTWOOD c.1777

Hylands, Widford

The house built in the Queen Anne style 1728 – 30, from an engraving c.1770.

The east and west wings and elegant portico, possibly suggested by Humphry Repton, have yet to be added.

The map, surveyed 1772 – 74, shows a small c.100 acre wood-pasture estate surrounded by a park pale. The dashed line shows approximately the current boundary of the park. Note the site of Hooks, demolished in the 19th century, and the public roads crossing the estate, closed by later owner John Attwood in the 1840s. (Engraving c.1770, Map 1777).

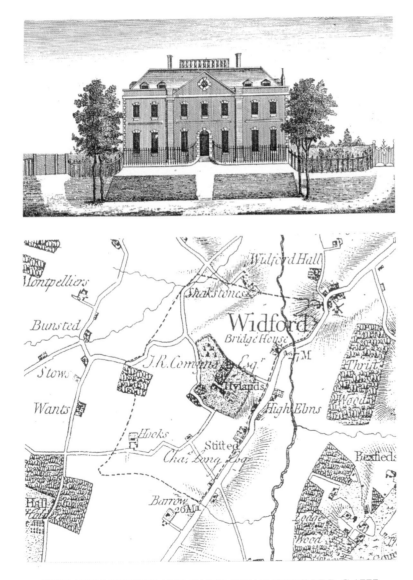

HYLANDS HOUSE AND PARK, NEAR WIDFORD C.1777

Estate Maps in the Essex Records Office

A list of maps which depict Essex parks from the Essex Record Office and listed in Emmison, F.G. (1947) Catalogue of Maps in the Essex Record Office 1566 – 1855 plus supplements.

KEY: M = EMMISON (1947)
      1 = SUPPLEMENT 1 (1952)
      2 = SUPPLEMENT 2 (1964)
      3 = SUPPLEMENT 3 (1968)

		SUPPLEMENT	PAGE NUMBERS
ARDLEIGH		2	29, 32
AUDLEY END	M		46, 78
		1	5, 19, 22, 29
		3	15, 23
BARRINGTON HALL		2	13
BELHUS	M		42, 78
BENTLEY	M		3
BENTLEY (GREAT) LODGE		2	33
BERDEN		2	17
BIFRONS	M		79
BOCKING HALL		2	26
BOREHAM HOUSE	M		37, 54
BOWER HALL		2	15
BRAXTED (GREAT)	M		55
		3	3
BRITTENS		1	2
CHESTERFORD (LITTLE)		2	32
COPFORD HALL		2	17
CRONDON	M		1, 7, 39, 53
		2	34
DAGNAMS	M		16
DANBURY	M		18
		3	3
DEBDEN HALL		1	31
DUNMOW	M		5
EASTON (GREAT)		2	2
ELSENHAM		3	12
GIDEA HALL	M		30
		1	2
GOSFIELD		2	14
GREENSTEAD		2	20
HALLINGBURY PLACE		2	35
HANNINGFIELDS	M		41
HARLOW	M		23
		1	26
HAROLDS		1	1
HATFIELD PEVEREL	M		19
HAVERING		1	2, 25, 32
HAVERING-ATTE-BOWER	M		18
HEDINGHAM CASTLE		2	36
HEMPSTEAD		3	1
HIGHAM HOUSE		2	29

	SUPPLEMENT	**PAGE NUMBERS**
HORNDON (WEST)	M	2
HYLANDS	1	31
	2	27
	3	12
ILFORD (LITTLE)	1	12
INGATESTONE	M	32, 39
KELVEDON HATCH	1	19
LANGFORD GROVE	3	21
LANGLEY	2	17
LAWFORD	2	20
LEXDEN	M	37
LEYTON	M	81
LITTLEBURY	M	44
MARKS HALL	2	38
	3	5
MARSHALLS	1	32
MISTLEY	M	23, 24
MOULSHAM HALL	M	1
	3	13
NAVESTOCK	M	36
NAZEING	3	20
NEW HALL	M	54
ONGAR	1	28
	2	22
OSYTH (SAINT)	M	60
	2	12, 26
PYRGO	M	79
	1	2
QUENDON	1	7
RIVENHALL	M	10, 35
SHENVILLES	M	1
SHORTGROVE	M	78
	1	19
	2	18
STANSTED HALL	2	19
STANWAY	M	29
STEWARDS	1	2
TERLING	1	1, 17
THORNDON	M	13, 23, 30, 31
WALDEN (LITTLE)	1	22
WALTHAM HOLY CROSS	1	1
WANSTEAD	M	12, 15, 32, 33, 86
	1	18, 29
	3	10, 11, 12, 18, 19, 20
WEALD	M	15, 16
WIDDINGTON	1	4
WINTREY	1	4
WIVENHOE	M	14
	2	12, 34
WOODFORD	2	22
WRITTLE	2	34

Four Essex Parks from the Chapman and André Map of 1777

WEALD

In existence now for over 700 years, still shows the park lodge with far-reaching views over most of the park. Also, but slightly misplaced, is the Belvedere built in the 1740s and later enlarged by the Tower family adjacent to the church. The south-east corner of the park is today probably the best place in Essex to get the feel of a medieval deer park.

MISTLEY PARK

Unusually sited for a park on the exposed banks of the Stour near Manningtree, is noticeably surrounded by dense belts of woodland on three sides, presumably as some sort of shelter from high winds. The windmill (top right-hand corner) was, however, presumably sited to take advantage of them. Although now disparked, Mistley is still home to 'old knobbly', an oak pollard with a girth of 32ft 8ins – the second largest in Essex.

EASTON PARK NEAR DUNMOW

Easton Park was well known for its fine treescape; note the four vistas, almost a patte d'oie, cut through the park. The 700 acre park held some 570 head of deer in the late 19th century, mostly Fallow, but also 120 Red. The park was virtually completely obliterated by the construction of an American bomber base in the second world war.

NEW HALL, BOREHAM

Home to Henry VIII's palace, partly demolished and much reduced in size in the 18th century and now a school. Note the double avenue of limes planted by John Tradescant the elder in 1624, but felled by 1800 and also the carriage turn-around. (Boreham House is also shown on this section of map).

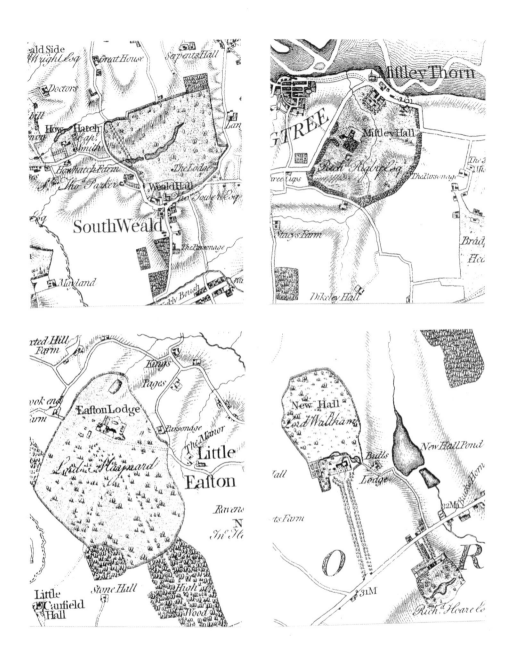

**FOUR ESSEX PARKS FROM THE CHAPMAN AND ANDRÉ MAP OF 1777.
WEALD, NEAR BRENTWOOD; MISTLEY, MANNINGTREE, EASTON, NEAR
GREAT DUNMOW AND NEW HALL, BOREHAM**

Fabulous Wanstead Park

Rocque's plan of 1745 shows the magnificent, complex and elaborate gardens at Wanstead dating from the late 17th century. They were created by Sir Josiah Child, Chairman of the East India Company, who had purchased the Wanstead estate in 1667. Sir Josiah spent a fortune on the park, but notably not the house.

He died in 1699 and his son (also Josiah) inherited the estate, but died not long after, in 1704. The property passed to his half-brother, Richard Child, later Viscount Castlemain (1718) and Earl Tylney (1733). He continued the landscaping of the park and also commissioned the architect Colen Campbell to produce the plan for the famous palladian mansion – Wanstead House - in 1715. The Rocque plan shows some water features that were never actually fully finished in the park (ie the straight canal due east of the house), but much of it is as surveyed later by Chapman and André in 1772 – 4. The remains of Wanstead Park, now about 140 acres, were acquired the by The Corporation of London and eventually formally opened to the public as part of Epping Forest in 1882.

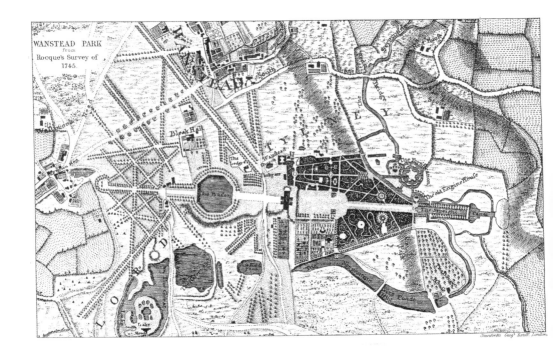

ROCQUE'S PLAN FROM HIS SURVEY OF LONDON 1744-46
(PREVIOUSLY SURVEYED C.1735). SEE ALSO PAGE 180.

The Extent of Essex Parks

Cantor, writing in 1983, suggests that the medieval park was probably between 100 and 200 acres. In this publication I have suggested a figure of around 250 acres as the average size for a park. I have found many parks in Essex within this range – Danbury (1282) 123 acres, Bedfords (15th century) 215, Gidea (1462) 200, Harold's (1225) 200, Thundersley (1254) 250. However, of 23 medieval parks in Essex for which I had a calculated or good estimate for their extent, an average figure of 449 acres (181 ha) was calculated.

Of these 23 parks, 11 were under 250 acres, whilst four were well over 8 – 900 acres. These four sizeable parks, as far as I am aware, were the largest parks in Essex. Rayleigh (c.800 – 1,000), Crondon (c.1,000), Ongar (1,200) and Havering, the largest of all Essex Parks, 1,300 acres. This will have led to an inflated average figure for Essex Parks. When a total of 34 Essex park acreages from all periods was calculated and averaged (medieval, Tudor, Stuart and Georgian), an average figure of 420 acres (170 ha) was achieved. Possibly larger Essex parks are more prominent in the historic record.

The issue of park size is further complicated by what can readily be admitted to be the minimum (or indeed maximum) size for a park. Oliver Rackham records a fourteen acre Barking Park in Suffolk (big enough for just a dozen or so deer), whilst Lancaster Great Park in Sussex (better known today as Ashdown Forest) was said to cover 13,500 acres and was surrounded by a ditch and bank with a fence some 34 miles in extent with around 40 gates in it. Fourteen acres is barely "extensive grounds", whilst Lancaster Great Park was over twice the size of Epping Forest and thirteen times the size of Hatfield Forest.

The extent of individual parks can also vary greatly, over time being enlarged or partially disparked, depending on the financial (or political) circumstances or whim of the owner. A 200 acre park in 1340 might be a 450 acre park by 1545 and partially disparked to 325 acres in 1730, but gone completely by 1850.

There are odd records of parks which seem to have been created to keep deer out, rather than in, such as the deer-proof fence which has been erected at Marks Hall, Coggeshall today. This has been done to protect the many plants and trees in the new arboretum. Similarly in 1285 Reginald de Gynges was licensed to empark "20 ac. wood, 10 ac. laund, 1 ac. garden in Ingrave [near Brentwood] round his court there, notwithstanding that the deer repair there by reason of the density of his wood". This "park" of 31 acres is the smallest I have come across in the county. In not, apparently, being created for retaining deer, it pre-empts the present day park movement.

Buildings and other structures within Parks

The first and most obvious structure needed for a deer park was the pale, a fence of cleft oak which surrounded the entire perimeter of the park, its purpose to contain the deer. The pale would have breaks for gates (hatches) and sometimes a deer-leap (saltory). Deer-leaps are recorded at least for Wanstead, Writtle and Havering Parks. They allowed deer to get into the park, but not out. The perimeter fence, usually surmounted on a bank and ditch, was an expensive undertaking, hence the rounded oblong shape typical of early parks, classically seen in Ongar Great Park.

The second most important structure within the park would have been the lodge. The presence of large numbers of poachable deer within the park would have required the permanent presence of an individual to look after the deer, the parker, who oversaw and ran the park from the lodge. Most, if not all, deer parks must have had at least one lodge situated usually in a position from where most of the park could be seen. Many parks had just one lodge, even the large 1,200 acre (500 ha.) Ongar Park. Some giant parks, such as Clarendon Park (4,000 acres = 1,666 ha.) in Wiltshire had three lodges. Lodges were prevalent in the early medieval period before grand houses and manor houses came to be situated in parks.

One early park in Essex was the Royal Park of Hadleigh. Hadleigh Castle was built in c.1230. The park was licensed shortly afterwards, in 1235, but it was emparked on land adjacent to the castle. It may have been that the deer park was seen as very much a working component of a much larger landholding, comprising farmland, vineyard, woodland, water mill and fisheries. Hadleigh Park is recorded as having a park lodge in 1366, being repaired then along with the pale.

A recent excavation of farmland west of Stansted Airport (and immediately north of Hatfield Forest) has revealed what is almost certainly a lodge occupied from the 14th to the 18th centuries. Originally it was a simple timber-framed hall with a later wing added to create an 'L' shaped building, then having what was probably a bake-house or kitchen detached from the main structure built. Smaller ancillary buildings – possibly stables or barns – were also found. The buildings were thought to have been demolished and the site cleared in the 18th century. It was the small finds which gave a clue to the buildings' possible original use, including many objects to do with horse furniture and hunting, including harness fittings, various forms of arrow head, spurs and horseshoes. The excavated bone assemblage also included equal amounts of sheep, cattle and fallow deer remains. It is possible that the building started life as a park lodge, but eventually became a farm when the land was disparked.

The Royal Park of Havering was disparked and sold in 1652, the two lodges being described thus – "Great Lodge consisting of a hall, a kitchen, two parlours, butteries, with other necessary rooms with chambers over them, with a barn and stable – we value at one hundred pounds. The Little Lodge consisting of a hall, a kitchen, a parlour and chambers over them, with a barn and stable……..we value at forty pounds". The Little Lodge may have been the earlier of the two buildings; it was described as a "ruinous tenement". The lodges were probably a standard design, built to cater for the needs of housing the parker and assorted huntsmen, horses and dogs when they came to take the deer in the park.

Littley Park Farmhouse (still extant) near Leez Priory, shows three phases of building, of which the earliest c1470 is thought to be the original park lodge, later added to in the 16th and 17th centuries, eventually becoming the farmhouse when the park reverted to agricultural land. Littley Park was disparked in phases – it survived in part as a deer park into the 18th century, but was gone completely by 1777.

Nazeing Wood, emparked in 1542 for £132, had a lodge and standing built for the sum of just £13 15s 1/2d. Obviously these two buildings were not meant to be as enduring as the famous 'Queen Elizabeth's Hunting Lodge' – a standing built for Henry VIII when he emparked 'Fayremeade' near Chingford in Epping Forest in 1542. The cost of paling, parokes and standing(s) is stated as £1,500. The standing was a partly open building from where the King and his guests could view a ritual hunt. The parokes are an enclosure where deer were kept before being driven towards the standing to be slaughtered by the King and his retinue. Fairmead Park and nearby Waltham Park were just two of numerous parks created by Henry VIII in the later years of his life. Many had a very brief life – Fairmead probably only 12 years, Waltham even less; started in 1542, it was still being constructed in 1543 and was disparked in 1548, a year after Henry's death.

In 1543 the lodge of Waltham Park was under construction, being built adjacent to the park gate. There are records of payments to bricklayers raising walls and building chimneys and to carpenters making the timber frame. The nearby Waltham Abbey was obviously being demolished, as there are payments for carting 'olde timber' out of the 'cherche yeard' for re-use in the construction of the lodge.

One intriguing reference in the accounts is to the making of twelve 'sawpitts in the olde park'. The sawpits were probably for cutting logs into usable structural timber and planking for floors – the old park is possibly a smaller, earlier park – Cantor mentions a Waltham Park of 1335 owned by the Waltham Monks, or it is possibly a reference to nearby Harold Park (extant c.1200) and also owned by the Abbey (Public Records Office). Lodge Farmhouse at Galleywood, a 13th century building, is said to be a lodge and standing combined, later converted to a farmhouse.

Although many parks have disappeared almost without trace, there are numerous clues to the possible existence of a former park. The names Park Farm or Lodge Farm are frequent and also the park and lodge element recorded in field names is also very common. The probable lodge near Stansted Airport discussed earlier, has the name Park Barn Field and also Bury Lodge and Little Bury Lodge Farm nearby, indicating again the possible origin of the building.

Lord Braybrooke (1836) refers to an "ancient Hunting-tower" demolished to make way for the Robert Adam designed 'Temple of Victory' (1771 – 1772) on Ring Hill, an Iron Age hill fort overlooking Audley End. This may have been a very early hunt viewing platform, similar in design and function to the extant Cage at Lyme Park in Cheshire, or the stand at Chatsworth, the latter being built about 1582 for Bess of Hardwick. As such, it may well have been unique in Essex.

Bodies of water are a recurring feature of many parks, presumably originally constructed to water livestock (sheep and cattle, as well as deer). The medieval love of multiple land uses may have caused some of these to become fish-ponds as well. There are numerous references to the fish-pond in Havering Park. In 1232, Simon de Everdon, Archdeacon of Chester, was granted 40 bream to stock his fish-pond at Aungre (Ongar). On the same date, a further 180 bream were granted to various other individuals (carp had not yet been introduced to Britain). Also in 1232, the King's fisherman was sent to Havering with six casks (dolia) to pick-up bream to stock the King's fish-ponds in London.

Spains Hall, Finchingfield, had a chain of seven, one-acre ponds near the house. Arthur Young transcribed the results of "experiments", by the owner Thomas Ruggles, in fish husbandry in his general view of the Agriculture of the County of Essex in 1807. Tench were by far the commonest fish reared, followed by carp, but a few eel and perch are recorded too. The interconnected ponds were stocked with small fish and then emptied (drawn down) two, three or four years later and the fish weighed to give an idea of their productivity.

Arthur Young (1807) also mentions the ponds of Leez Priory in connection with their neglect; "There is a chain of them near a mile in length and occupying about thirty acres, which were once under water, formed and sluiced with great attention and a stream through them, but at present, and for many years past, water in only two of them, and those almost choked-up with mud by neglect". Pond Park, north of Leez Priory, is said to have taken its name from these ponds. Pond-head Field and Crotch Pond Mead, totalling about 45 acres, are named on a 1775 estate map located by a loop in the River Ter and they commemorate these ponds. The ponds are still clearly marked on modern Ordnance Survey Maps (Pathfinder 1098 – Great and Little Waltham). The ponds were said to have been constructed much earlier by the monks as dual fish and mill ponds.

Some of these park ponds would later have been enlarged or altered and incorporated into landscape schemes – the Spains Hall ponds were the subject of a suggested alteration by Humphry Repton in 1807. The pond in the walled kitchen garden at Hylands is marked as a fish pond on the 1878 Ordnance Survey Map. I can only think the presence of the small, but deep, pond in the kitchen garden would have been to provide fresh fish for the table.

Carp (above) Tench (below), the two favoured species for park ponds. In medieval Havering, before the introduction of Carp, Bream are the species mentioned.

Many parks also had moated sites within their bounds, possibly the sites of ancient, long-gone, manor houses, the house demolished and their land incorporated into the park. Many of these moats could no doubt have provided fish, as well as originally a means of defence. The 1775 estate map of Pond Park also includes mention of a Decoy Field. It is not beyond the bounds of possibility that the extensive ponds attracted numerous wild-fowl and that a duck decoy was made to harvest them. I know of only one other park with decoys in Essex (they were a common feature of the Essex coast), Navestock, recorded on an estate map dated 1726. The 1775 Pond Park estate map also shows a Deer house Field, possibly a reference to a Deer-shelter, which occurred in other parks (and Epping Forest, as in Deer-shelter Plain).

Rabbit warrens, with their distinctive pillow mounds, were another feature, particularly of medieval parks, but many had been ploughed-up by the 18th century – by which time rabbits had become all too well adapted to the English climate and become a pest, hence their exclusion from landscaped parks. Essex, in Rayleigh and Thundersley Parks, had two of the earliest known warrens. The middens at Rayleigh Castle (in royal hands 1163 – 1215, empty by 1220) were found to have some of the earliest rabbit remains in England.

Two small building types often encountered in parks are dove-cotes and ice-houses. Dove-cotes are known from Marks Hall, Castle Hedingham, Ingatestone Hall, Quendon, Langleys, Writtle and Shortgrove; Quendon's octagonal dove-cote probably dates from before the 16th century. Writtle's dove-cote is said to be the only circular dove-cote in Essex.

Ice-houses, packed with ice in winter to provide ice and cold-storage for later in the year, are a feature of many parks, including Blake Hall, Braxted, Gidea Hall and Hylands. The ice-house at Gidea Hall was said to have been designed by Richard Woods. The ice-house at Hylands was allegedly destroyed in army explosives practise during the second world war.

Ingatestone Hall (the short-lived park, disparked by 1605), has provided the only record of a mews, a place where falcons and hawks used for hawking were kept. Sir William Petre employed a falconer, Edmund Bell, who is mentioned buying bells, jesses and hoods in 1550. Petre kept goshawks (and sparrow hawks) as befitted his status. Falcons were probably kept at Belhus Park in the 19th century.

As is often the case in Essex, the abundant London Clay which underlies the county was a good source of clay for brick-making. Because of their size, many brick-built mansions had their own brick-kilns, established, presumably by itinerant brick-makers nearby. The legacy of this is often to be found in field and wood names. Albyns has a Brick Clamp Field. Belhus has its Brick-Kiln Wood (established by 1619). Hylands has two fields – Brick Field (273) and Clay Pit Field (307) mentioned in the Writtle Parish tithe award for 1839 and Stansted Hall has its Brick Kiln Spring.

Thus the splendid houses of the rich and powerful upper classes came to be built in parks, the fashion for keeping deer waned and lodges became redundant, or their purpose became subsumed within other utility buildings in the park. With the great houses came all the necessary buildings to run the park and estate, such as stable blocks and home farms. Hatch Farm at Thorndon Hall was built as a 'model farm', fashionable at the time to farm deer and cattle. With many parks being disparked in the late 17th and 18th centuries, many lodges must have become the farmhouse from which the land was later farmed and probably many survive undiscovered in Essex today. Farming rents by this time were much more profitable than deer and the status conferred by ownership of a deer park was less significant.

The trend towards landscaped parks in the 18th century led to an increased use of the ha- ha. Probably French in origin, they were designed to keep livestock from straying into the garden area around the house, without restricting or blocking the view across the park as a traditional fence would. The ha-ha occurred in many parks and even some smaller gardens had them. They are known from Audley End, Weald Park (bulldozed out in the 1950s), St Osyth, Terling Place, Blake Hall and other Essex Parks. Hylands has had two; one probably by Humphry Repton on the north side of Hylands House, now filled in, and another created south of the house by Christine Hanbury in the 1920s.

Hylands eventually incorporated a Home Farm. By 1854 this consisted of a barn, stable, cow house, cow shed, piggeries, hay house, cart lodge and slaughterhouse. The Home Farm was situated some distance from the house and stable-block, but still within walking distance. Garden buildings at this time included a large greenhouse and a walled kitchen garden with peach houses, pineries, potting sheds and gardeners' cottage; a bothy is also mentioned at a later date.

A plan of Hylands House by Chancellor and Son of Chelmsford made in 1907 shows an extensive complex of small utilitarian buildings and rooms situated between the main house and the stable block. The buildings included kennels, wood and coal stores, carpenters shop, laundry, ironing room, game larder, larder, lamp room, brush room, kitchen, scullery, stores, servants hall and dairy. Dry rot was discovered extensively in these buildings and they were demolished completely in 1971.

There are a few building types that are rare in parks. A medieval (13th century) wooden chapel is recorded for Littley Park near Leez Priory. It was still extant and used as a barn in 1575. Presumably the many large houses later incorporated chapels for their owners' spiritual well-being. Churches also occasionally occur in parks, presumably due to later emparking. Chapman and André (1777) show Gosfield and East Donyland Parks with churches within the confines of the park pale. Braxted Church is shown on Chapman and André 1777 map as being outside the park pale. When Braxted's wall was constructed 1825 – 31 and the park enlarged to the west and east, it was incorporated into the park. The long-gone Woodham Walter Hall had an adjacent medieval church moved away from the house in 1563. Chapman and André show a windmill at Mistley Hall within the park pale. Copped Hall is unique in England in having a miniature rackets court (c.1895) adjacent to the house. Rolls Park, Chigwell has an orangery.

Many parks had gate lodges. Havering Park (around 1410) had an important entrance in 'Southgate' and a keeper was appointed, presumably residing in a gate-lodge nearby. One is mentioned in the sales particulars for the park in 1650. Crowgate Cottage, recently investigated and on the perimeter of Littley Park, south of Leez Priory and adjacent to the Causeway, a bridleway leading to the priory, was constructed c1570 – 1590. It is almost certainly a gate-lodge (not the later residence of the parker, as suggested, since the views of the park would then have been obscured by woodland). Hylands, according to a sales brochure of 1922, lists four gate lodges, all but Writtle Lodge, now a private residence, demolished.

Parks that still exist in something like their ancient form and have not been affected by modern intensive agricultural practises, are often good sites for searching for evidence of human occupation before emparking. Lawford Hall has a Bronze Age barrow; Audley End has its Ring Hill Camp; South Weald also has what is probably an Iron Age Hill Fort and Crondon, although farmed (and golfed), has a massive earthwork (at TL 689001), which may also be part of an ancient fortification. Lexden Park near Colchester also has ancient earthworks – a huge ditch and bank said to be an Iron Age defensive position is now a scheduled ancient monument.

The Hunting Tower at Audley End demolished c.1770

Grazing Animals in Parks

The principal beast of the medieval park was the fallow deer, probably introduced by the Normans to stock forests and parks. Other much less frequently encountered park beasts were the native red and roe deer, semi-wild park cattle and wild swine. The vast majority of Essex parks were stocked with fallow deer.

Deer were a prized item. They were something money could not buy and were a sought-after gift from the Crown or other owner of the park. There are numerous records of deer given as gifts by the Crown from Havering Park, often only in small number – two or three for the Queen of Scotland in 1238 – but sometimes much larger quantities. In December 1241 and January 1242, a total of 219 deer were taken from Havering Park and neighbouring Hainault Forest, of which 140 came from the park. The majority of these deer were eaten at feasts – Christmas, Easter and the fortnight of St Hilary are mentioned. Other deer from this total were taken as gifts, often with the number of animals being stipulated. On January 8th 1242, Simon de Chelefield was permitted to take 10 does in the park "of the King's gift". In December 1238 Richard de Muntfichet was ordered to take 80 does and 40 bucks (alive) for the Count of Flanders, presumably to start a forest or deer park there.

The actual taking of deer for feasts was undertaken by professional huntsmen. William Luvel and William May are recorded as huntsmen (vadletti) in 1236 at Havering Park, being required to take 50 does, salt the meat and transport it to Westminster. Ten does were taken from Havering in 1251 to be used at the feast of the enthronement of the Bishop of Rochester. The demand for salted venison at Havering was presumably the reason for a salting house being ordered to be made in 1228.

I suspect that little or no hunting took place in smaller parks, unless on foot. It would take probably just a couple of minutes to gallop across a 250 acre park on horseback and would also "stress-out" the non-target deer. Livestock other than deer (ie sheep or cattle) would also make it impossible to hunt some parks. Hunting on horseback may have taken place in very large parks, for example Havering (1,300 acres), but again when no domestic stock were in the park.

The carrying capacity of Havering Park (a park of 1,300 acres = 542 ha.) for deer is twice mentioned at 1,200 animals – around one per acre – and this not including any domestic livestock pastured in the park. In practice the number may have been much lower than this. However, in March 1251 – probably following a very hard winter – hay was ordered to be brought-in for the deer, but by April it was ordered that the dead deer and swine rotting in the park should be removed and buried (notably no domestic stock is mentioned).

Wild swine were ordered to be brought to Havering Park by Thomas de Langley, Keeper of the Forest of Wychwood in 1223. Domestic pigs were also kept in the park, sometimes with the instruction that they had rings in their noses to prevent them from rooting-up the park. Presumably the domestic swine hybridised eventually with the wild, or it is possible that the wild swine were kept in a separate enclosure within the park. In September 1234 it was ordered that all hogs in the park for pannage were to be slaughtered and salted.

Cattle were also grazed in the park; in some instances the grazing at Havering was rented out. The park keeper of Little Lodge was permitted to keep 24 cows and one bull in the park in the 17th Century. In 1223 it was ordered that 50 lean oxen were to be fattened at Havering for the feast of St Martin. Later in 1260 it was requested that 200 cattle be put on the park to "eat up the old grass".

By 1652, when Havering was disparked and eventually sold, there were just two hundred deer "of several sorts". Interestingly, they were given a value of £200. At the same time the vicar of Hornchurch, who usually received a buck and a doe per year, had his gift commuted to a value of £5.00. There are many instances of deer (Red and Fallow) being poached from Essex parks.

Wild swine, apart from being found at Havering, were also recorded as late as the 1520s – 1530s in the emparked Chalkney Wood near Earls Colne. One entry related to Havering Park in 1240 indicates red deer were present; an order was made for 12 bucks (fallow) and two stags (red). The 126+ parks of the medieval period in Essex had dwindled to just nine functional deer parks by 1892. All these parks had fallow deer, but three also had red deer - Easton (120), Thorndon (40) and Weald (70). Sika (9) and Roe (2) deer are also recorded for Weald Park. Although Hylands now has a herd of around one hundred head of fallow deer - mainly nocturnal visitors to the park - it seems that no deer were present in the park in 1892, just domestic livestock. An engraving of Hylands House dated 1854 does, however, show a small herd of fallow deer in front of the house. The modern herd of fallow deer at Hylands (probably shared with Writtle Forest) are really at Hylands by default. They access the park through the non deer-proof parts of the western boundary of the estate. There is a deer-proof fence between the lower Belt and the neighbouring golf course at Webbs Farm.

Muntjac, an introduction from Asia, is also present in small numbers at Hylands today. Nearby Writtle deer park – now disparked and consisting of vast arable fields – actually still has a sizeable herd of fallow deer at times on its ground . Muntjac are also present in Writtle Forest. Fallow deer herds have now built-up to high numbers in Essex. They are even moving into urban areas, such as Harold Hill, near Romford, to feed in gardens. There are deer warning signs in place on the outskirts of Harold Hill not far from Dagnam Park.

White park cattle were, until recently, kept at Thorndon Park, but currently has a small herd of shorthorn cattle. Longhorn cattle are present at Marks Hall, a small group (around 6) from the Chalkney Mill herd. Young in 1807 writes of longhorn cattle kept at Rochetts, South Weald.

Horses are much under-recorded in parks, but as the principal means of transport up to the early 20th century, they must have occurred at some time in all parks. The earliest records I know of, are of horses being reared at studs at Hadleigh and Rayleigh Parks in the reign of Edward II in the very early 14th century. A statute of 1535 made it compulsory for park owners to maintain studs for breeding horses, even stipulating the number of brood mares and also the size of the horse (15hh for stallions and 13hh for mares). John Halfhead, Keeper of Havering Park, was permitted to keep six horses there in the 17th century, presumably for patrolling the 1300 acre park. The stable block at Hylands, dating from the early 19th century, had a number of stall stables and loose boxes and could accommodate up to 20 horses. Carriage and draught horses, the latter in the Home Farm, were present at Hylands and I assume that hunters (Arthur Pryor, a Victorian owner of Hylands was a noted huntsman in his time) would also have been stabled there. The horses would have grazed and been fed on hay from the park – possibly a reason why so much grassland and meadow survives in the park today. The third Lord Braybrooke at Audley End was a horse-racing enthusiast and a number of famous racehorses were bred here, including 'Sir Joshua', winner of the 1000 Guineas in 1816. A number of ponies and horses currently graze Stansted Hall park.

The 18th century was a great period of agricultural improvement in Britain. Many parks became disparked at this time. The perceived need to improve agricultural quality and yield may have contributed to this. Thorndon Hall's Hatch Farm was created around 1777 as a 'model farm' to raise deer and cattle.

Thorndon in the 18th century, according to Arthur Young, was a park of 1,077 acres. Its livestock were listed as:

800 deer (Probably Fallow and Red)
850 sheep and lambs (Norfolk/South Down cross)
 22 cows (Holderness, Suffolk, Devon)
  8 working oxen
 30 bullocks
 20 young cattle

Jacob sheep are recorded at Audley End in the late 18th century, presumably for ornament. Norfolk and South Down sheep were kept at Skreens, Roxwell at this time; South Down sheep were also kept at Gosfield and in other parks.

John Conyers (II) kept a dairy herd of North Devon cattle at Copped Hall (as did Sir Richard Neave at Dagnam Park) producing butter, cream, cheese and milk and calves; Pigs are also mentioned here. Lord Braybrooke at Audley End kept polled Yorkshire cattle (the fifth Lord Braybrooke later kept a herd of pedigree Jersey cattle here). Cornelius Kortright at Hylands, also around this time, raised a new breed of sheep – a Merino/South Down cross, which produced very fine wool. It is likely these would have grazed the park. Sheep, cattle and pigs were all farmed at Hylands. It is not known if pigs were kept at large in the park. Livestock has been absent from Hylands since probably the late 1950s, although there are plans to introduce Suffolk Punch horses into the park to graze.

Sometimes exotic beasts were kept in parks. At Weald Park wild goats from Kashmir were introduced in 1823, the herd surviving until the 1930s. A pair were given to George IV in 1828, forming the basis of the famous herd at Windsor Great Park. A small herd of feral goats is currently to be found at Thorndon Park, in a fenced enclosure near the visitor centre. The animals are part of a grazing trial for conservation reasons. Two Indian Zebu cattle were also kept at Weald Park. Lord Braybrooke at Audley End had a five acre enclosure 'with a high paling' originally intended for a menagerie (as at Thorndon Park), but "stocked with gold and silver pheasants and some other curous birds".

At the turn of the last century, fallow deer were present enclosed in only three Essex parks – Quendon (where deer have now been kept for over 300 years), Weald Park and the Epping Forest deer sanctuary at Theydon Bois. Red deer have been 'farmed' in Essex, not strictly speaking in parks, but in enclosures. I have records of such ventures from Cock Clarks near Purleigh, Hartford End near Great Waltham and from Layer Marney Towers near Tiptree. Records of red deer at large from the Dunmow/Great Waltham area possibly originated from the Hartford End venture. Red Deer have been kept since the 1930s at Bedfords Park – numbering about 48 head (8 stags and 40 hinds) in October 2003. Roe deer have been seen recently in the Lyons Hall (near Little Leighs) area, around Terling Place and also at Marks Hall near Coggeshall, but not in enclosed parks.

From a fallow deer point of view, it could be argued that rural Essex, bounded by the A12, suburban London, the M11 and the county boundary to the north, has become one gigantic deer park.

The Great Oaks of Essex Parks and Other Trees

J.C.Shenstone – writing in Volume VIII of The Essex Naturalist of 1894 on the subject of the oak tree in Essex – included a number of sizeable and notable oak trees, the majority old pollards, that he had recorded in parks in the county. Many of the trees were girthed and some illustrated in the paper. Shenstone wrote of Danbury Park "I believe that I am justified in saying that the spot in all Essex richest in fine oak trees, is the park at Danbury". Here he notes at least two oak pollards with girths of 31ft, one of which he contends was at one time very much larger, part of the trunk having fallen away, and five others with girths of between 23ft and 27ft.

Other parks mentioned included Thorrington Hall, Alresford – with "four monster oak pollards" with trunks girthed at between 27ft and 31ft. At Barrington Hall, Hatfield Broad Oak, he records two pollards with girths of 29ft 6ins and 18ft 9ins. At Rivenhall Park near Witham and Mistley Hall near Manningtree, he noted several trees with girths of 21ft to 23ft. From a number of parks he recorded just single pollard trees – Lawford Hall near Manningtree (19ft 3ins), Skreens, Roxwell (26ft), Writtle Park near Margaretting (25ft) and Quendon Hall, Newport (20ft 2ins). Privately-owned Barrington Hall appears to have the largest Oak tree in Essex – a magnificent pollard girthed at just under 38 feet, measured in November 2003. This appears to be the oak measured by Shenstone. It also has other sizeable pollard oaks on what was the boundary of the park.

Danbury Park – a deer park since early medieval times – still has good numbers of ancient oak trees. In 1560 the park was said to be "……for the most part is well grown with timber of oaks". However, in the 19th century, many hundreds of trees – presumably mostly standards – were removed, firstly by the Church Commissioners, who purchased the park in 1845 as a residence for the Bishop of Rochester and later the Bishop of St Albans, and secondly by Hugh Hoare, a later owner who felled some 430 trees between 1892 and 1903. Interestingly at least two of the pollards at Danbury are pollarded at a great height – around 12ft – (3.66m).

Thorndon Park still has a number of fine pollard trees, but their numbers are much depleted. Very little remains of the "2,080 oak pollards and 1,323 hornbine trees" recorded in a survey of 1774 on Childerditch Common, before it was incorporated into the park around 1800. I did, however, girth one surviving oak from this era at 17ft 10ins, being located south of the visitor centre.

Weald Park still has good numbers of ancient pollard oaks – the old deer park (the south-east corner) has a concentration of very large oak pollards, several being over 20ft in girth. This part of the park currently fenced and grazed by cattle (but also wild deer and rabbits) is probably the nearest we have to the appearance of a medieval deer park in Essex. It has everything (apart from a park pale) one would expect in a medieval wood-pasture – ancient pollard oaks, the odd hornbeam pollard, grassy launds, patches of bracken, some sizeable standard oaks, patches of secondary woodland and even an old alder slade with sizeable alder stools and standard trees.

The rest of the park is well-wooded with numerous mixed plantations, including many conifers (Crossbills are recorded here). A tame herd of fallow deer is kept in an enclosure by the visitor centre; it totalled about 36 head (including fawns) in July 2003.

Mistley Park (now disparked) in the north of the county near Manningtree, in the part now known as Furze Hill, has a concentration of the largest old pollard oaks in Essex; there are at least a dozen here with girths between 15ft and 32ft 8ins. The latter is the second largest pollard oak in Essex, affectionately known as 'old knobbly' – the tree even has its own web site.

Two parks that Shenstone never seems to have visited are Lexden and Wivenhoe, both on the outskirts of Colchester. Lexden only partly survives – the extant section contains the Lexden Dyke, an immense Iron Age defensive ditch and bank and a scheduled ancient monument. It was this structure that probably saved the park from being swallowed-up by housing development. The park has a number of huge pollard Oaks 18 – 19ft in girth, plus an immense pollarded Beech and pollarded Sweet Chestnut. Not all the remaining park is part of the local nature reserve – some is privately owned. The area containing the dyke itself is being allowed to scrub over to protect it, but at the expense of the grassy laund of the medieval park.

Wivenhoe Park now houses Essex University (since 1964); the university halls of residence and other buildings provide an incongruous backdrop to the ancient pollard trees of the old park. There are a number of pollard oaks, particularly noticeable around the university playing fields, together with an immense pollard (g.b.h. 27ft) near the lake. I suspect that both Lexden and Wivenhoe Parks would have significant assemblages of saproxylic invertebrates.

Pond Park (private, but traversed by footpaths) near Leez Priory, disparked in the 18th century, still has at least one remaining substantial oak tree. It is not on a hedge line, but stands in the middle of a field. I estimated its girth at around 20ft. There are, however, quite a number of old pollard ash trees in hedgerows, or on old hedge lines, at least one of which may be a park boundary pollard. I also recorded two sizeable field maple pollards, one of which again may be a park boundary tree. Littley Park (also private, but with footpaths) near Leez Priory, is now mostly undistinguished arable farmland (it was a well-wooded park at one time). It does, however, have some pasture grazed by cattle (and still fallow deer) and in this area (TL 696168) visible from the footpath are a line of five pollard ash trees (estimated girth 13ft – 16ft), though once again whether these were present before the park was disparked is questionable. Similarly, a huge white willow pollard is to be found nearby (adjacent to the footpath) with a girth of 21ft 4ins.

Marks Hall, Coggeshall, had its ancient oak pollards survived, would today be one of the most important sites in Essex for veteran trees and saproxylic invertebrates. It is known that Thomas Phillips Price, who owned the estate from 1898 to 1932, left his third wife Mary Elizabeth only a life interest in the park. It is said that she never recovered from the shock of discovering this, and having retained the right to fell the timber, allowed the ancient trees to be cut down and the old park to be planted-up with conifers by the Forestry Commission (on a 999 year lease) in 1956. Only a handful of old pollards survive, including the Honywood Oak (gbh 28ft) and a sizeable Wild Service tree.

Weald, like many other parks, was also planted with exotic species of tree in the eighteenth and nineteenth centuries. It has the obligatory Wellingtonias (*Sequoiadendron giganteum*). One unusual park for planted trees is Gaynes Park, Upminster (Parklands). Not only does it have a huge native Black Poplar (*Populus nigra*), but it has a very fine collection of other poplars, sallows and willows (salicetum), some of which are now very sizeable, including what is probably the biggest Crack Willow (*Salix fragilis*) in Essex.

Trees noted here in 2003 included Silver Maple (*Acer saccharinum*), Tree of Heaven (*Ailanthus altissima*), Swamp Cypress (*Taxodium distichum*), Walnut (*Juglans regia*), some fine Plane trees (*Platanus acerifolia*) and two types of elm (*Ulmus procera* ('suckers') and a probable hybrid). The poplars, willows and sallows would seem to include Black Poplar (*Populus nigra*), Aspen (*P.tremula*), White Poplar (*P.alba*), Grey Poplar (*P. x canescens*), Lombardy Poplar (*P. nigra* f.*italica*), Hybrid Poplar (*P. x canadensis* var *serotina*), Balsam Poplar (*P.trichocarpa*), the willows

Salix fragilis, S.alba, S.viminalis, a weeping willow (*S.* x *pendulina*), and *S.* x *reichardtii*. Perhaps the most unusual tree is the cut-leaved variety of Alder (*Alnus glutinosa* var *laciniata*) near the old ornamental bridge. Notably at Gaynes, an old oak from the park survives in an adjacent garden.

Stansted Hall in the west of the county has an astonishing treescape, with Wellingtonias in quantity – particularly in the garden area, but liberally dotted about the park. It also has many fine specimen trees, including Redwood, Black Mulberry, London Plane, Scots Pine, Robinia, Tulip Tree, Holm Oak (possibly including var. Bicton), Beech (pollard), Box, Sycamore (pollards), Cedar of Lebanon and Fern-leaved Beech (*Fagus sylvatica* 'Heterophylla'). Notably it also has what is the largest Sweet Chestnut (a pollard, girth 24ft 7.5ins) I have so far come across in Essex. The park also contains much dead wood (up to whole trees) and is still grazed by a number of horses and ponies and the odd bullock. It is likely to be another important site for saproxylic invertebrates in Essex.

The grounds of Wivenhoe House (now a hotel) have two ancient (but unmeasurable) Cork Oaks (*Quercus suber*) said to have been brought back by General Rebow from his Peninsular War campaign in 1814.

List of Trees Commonly Found in Essex Parks

Acer pseudoplatanus	*Pinus sylvestris*
Aesculus hippocastanum	*Platanus* x *hispanica*
Cedrus libani	*Quercus ilex*
Fagus sylvatica	*Quercus robur*
Fraxinus excelsior	*Sequoiadendron giganteum*
Larix decidua	*Tilia* x *vulgaris*

The above tree species seem to crop-up regularly in lists of trees and shrubs from Essex parks. Sycamore and Plane are surprisingly frequent as pollard, as well as standard trees. Horse Chestnut also seems to be ubiquitous as a parkland tree – presumably because it is easy to propagate, quick to grow and stunningly beautiful when in full flower. Wellingtonia, introduced to cultivation in 1853, was a 'must have' fashion tree of Victorian times, planted in sizeable (and not so sizeable!) parks and gardens. Beech is a good landscape prop, due to its light-grey smooth bark and billowing outline. I assume that species such as Larch, Scots Pine and Oak (as standards) were planted for effect, but ultimately for their timber. Holm Oak, a native of the Mediterranean, is also surprisingly frequent in Essex parks. Braxted has a fine avenue of them, Stansted Hall has some very fine standard trees and Havering Park has a couple of good sized pollards.

Problem areas for some trees in parks, particularly those that have been encroached upon by urban development and are therefore accessible, include persistent vandalism. In Dagnam Park, Harold Hill, several old trees (including a probable 18ft+ girth ancient, hollow oak) have been set fire to and destroyed. Even 'old knobbly' at Mistley, our second largest Essex Oak, has been the victim of attempts to set fire to it. Elsewhere I have also seen trees ring-barked and others sprayed with graffiti. However, this damage is dwarfed by the ravages of some diseases, notably Dutch elm disease, which has destroyed most of our best ancient elms. The classic example of this is the mile and a half long elm avenue along the causeway at Littley Park near Great Waltham (shown on the Chapman and Andre map of 1777). Planted probably some 300 years ago, the trees succumbed to the disease in the 1970s and today just a few gaunt, dead, shorn, pollards remain near Littley Park farmhouse. The famous Wych Elm avenue at Gaynes was obviously destroyed by housing development. In many former parks, old trees have been removed in the interests of agricultural efficiency; it is difficult to manoeuvre bulky machinery around them and huge pollard limbs can damage tractor cabs. They also tend to shade surrounding crops.

The ancient oaks of medieval Terling Park (in existence by 1230) are visible from the road from Terling Hall Farm to Terling Village (centred on TL 770143). These old trees, some with girths over 20ft, now sit in cultivated farmland. Like many trees in such a situation, they are not prospering, many have significant die-back and some are completely dead. Oak die-back has been known in Britain since the 1970s; its causes are uncertain, but it seems likely that something is affecting the trees mycorrhizal fungi, inhibiting their ability to protect the root system of the tree, possibly climate (ie drought, or excessive winter rainfall) is involved, but other factors could be excessive nitrogen in the environment or even a cocktail of chemicals leaching through the soil horizon to affect the mycorrhizae.

Recent storms, such as those in 1987 and 1990, have taken their toll on Essex parkland trees. Some trees, such as Beech with their shallow root-plates, are particularly vulnerable, moreso if they are top-heavy pollards. Storms are nothing new to Essex; in March 1240 the Sheriff of Essex was ordered to put the King's houses at Havering into repair after being partly fallen and partly damaged by wind and tempest. Lord Braybrooke writing in 1836 "During the tremendous gale which occurred on the 31st of August 1833, and lasted twelve hours, upwards of five hundred and forty trees were blown down upon the Audley End Estate".

Perhaps I should mention here the field of pollard oaks at Mundon Hall, near Maldon. Depicted on the Chapman and Andre map of 1777 and surveyed by Shenstone in the late 19th century, there were 50 oaks recorded here in a small field. Apparently not strictly speaking a park, but more akin to the fields of pollard trees growing on the Breckland Edge, such as that at Risby in Suffolk. I visited the site in July 2003 and found just 28 trees, 25 of which were dead with 3 moribund, but producing small amounts of leaf. I would guess that cattle pastured beneath the trees have been overstocked and de-barked all the trees (the trees appear as white, barkless ghosts in full sunlight). It is one of the most extraordinary veteran tree sights in Essex, but the eventual loss of these pollard trees to future generations much saddens me.

Oak in Writtle Park 1894

Oak Pollards in Essex Parks (Surveyed 2000 – 2003) (girths measured, unless otherwise stated, at 1.3m = 4ft 3ins – the trees are all Quercus robur)

Danbury Park

TL 771048	7.52m	24ft 8ins
TL 770048	5.77m	18ft 11ins
TL 768053	6.00m	19ft 8ins

Hylands Park

TL 680045	6.11m	20ft 1ins
TL 680039	5.83m	19ft 2ins
TL 684034	4.76m	15ft 8ins

Mistley Park (Furze Hill)

TM 119311	9.96m	32ft 8ins
TM 119313	7.65m	25ft 1.5ins
TM 120311	6.40m	21ft
TM 119312	5.90m	19ft 4.5ins
TM 119311	4.66m	15ft 3.5ins

Skreens Park (Private)

TL 628076	6.92m	22ft 8.5ins
TL 632076	5.97m	19ft 7ins

Thorndon Park

TQ 615910	6.00m	19ft 8ins
TQ 606912	5.44m	17ft 10ins

Marks Hall

TL 839256	8.61m	28ft 3ins

Havering Park

TQ 505930	3.35m	11ft

Barrington Hall (Private)

TL 550178	11.51m	37ft 9ins

Weald Park

TQ 573944	6.76m	22ft 2.5ins
TQ 574944	6.54m	21ft 5.5ins
TQ 574945	6.25m	20ft 6ins
TQ 573944	6.02m	19ft 9ins
TQ 572945	5.97m	19ft 7ins
TQ 576943	5.95m	19ft 6ins
TQ 572945	5.60m	18ft 4.5ins

Pond Park (Private)

TL 696186	6.10m	20ft (estimated)

Warlies Park (Private)

TL 415016	6.00m	19ft 8ins
TL 418013	5.37m	17ft 7.5ins
TL 414017	4.84m	15ft 10.5ins

Hallingbury Park (Private)

TL 524193	4.75m	15ft 7ins

Wivenhoe Park (Essex University)

TM 031242	8.23m	27ft
TM 035238	6.77m	22ft 2.5ins
TM 035240	6.14m	20ft 1.5ins
TM 035240	4.57m	15ft

TM 035240		4.48m	14ft 8.5ins

Dagnam Park

TQ 550932		4.45m	14ft 7ins

Lexden Park

TL 972247		5.59m	18ft 4ins
TL 972247		5.54m	18ft 2ins
TL 971247		4.29m	14ft 1in

Hargrave House (Private)

TL 509255		5.76m	18ft 11ins

Stansted Hall (Private)

TL 520246		6.66m	21ft 10ins

Other notable specimen trees in Essex parks girthed at 1.3m:

Mistley Park

TM 119310	Alder	Pollard	3.94m	12ft 11ins
TM 118313	Oak	Standard	6.35m	20ft 9.5ins

Thorndon Park

TQ 615913	Oak	Standard	4.71m	15ft 5.5ins

Danbury Park

TL 767050	Sweet Chestnut	Standard	5.18m	17ft
TL 769052	Beech	Pollard	5.49m	18ft

Gaynes Park

TQ 555849	Black Poplar	Standard	4.46m	14ft 7.5ins

TQ 558850	Crack Willow	Pollard?	6.25m	20ft 6ins
TQ 559852	Alder (var laciniata)	Standard	2.60m	8ft 6.5ins

Marks Hall

TL 842263	Wild Service	Pollard	3.23m	10ft 7ins

Barrington Hall (Private)

TL 549175	Wellingtonia	Standard	6.20m	20ft 4ins

Weald Park

TQ 572942	Sweet Chestnut	Pollard	6.96m	22ft 10ins
TQ 576943	Hornbeam	Pollard	3.73m	12ft 3ins
TQ 573948	Beech (double-trunked)		5.12m	16ft 9.5ins
TQ 575946	Alder	Standard	3.30m	10ft 10ins

Littley Park (Private)

TL 693170	White Willow	Pollard	6.50m	21ft 4ins

Pond Park (Private)

TL 692186	Ash	Pollard	2.97m	9ft 9ins
TL 692186	Maple	Pollard	2.64m	8ft 8ins

Copped Hall (Private)

TL 429016	Redwood	Standard	3.61m	11ft 10ins
TL 429015	Swamp Cypress	Standard	3.20m	10ft 6ins
TL 428105	Hornbeam	Standard	3.28m	10ft 9ins
TL 428015	Hawthorn	Pollard	2.05m	6ft 8.5ins
TL 428015	Horse Chestnut	Pollard	4.67m	15ft 4ins
TL 430014	Holm Oak	Pollard	4.14m	13ft 7ins

Warlies (Private)

TL 414012	White Poplar	Standard	2.82m	9ft 3ins

Hallingbury Park (Private)

TL 523191	Beech	Pollard	5.74m	18ft 10ins
TL 523190	Beech	Pollard	5.78m	18ft 11.5ins

Bedfords

TQ 519924	Wellingtonia	Standard	5.16m	16ft 11ins
TQ 518928	Hybrid Poplar	Standard	5.20m	17ft 2.5ins

Lawford Hall (Private)

TM 089312	Oak	Standard	5.23m	17ft 2ins

Lexden Park

TL 972250	Holm Oak	Standard	3.43m	11ft 3ins

Stansted Hall (Private)

TL 519246	Sweet Chestnut	Pollard	7.51m	24ft 7.5ins
TL 522244	Scots Pine	Standard	3.43m	11ft 3ins
TL 524244	Robinia	Pollard	3.90m	12ft 9.5ins
TL 522241	Yew	Pollard	3.96m	13ft
TL 522242	Common Lime	Standard	4.78m	15ft 8.5ins
TL 523241	Wellingtonia	Standard	6.34m	20ft 9.5ins
TL 521243	Wellingtonia	Standard	4.91m	16ft 1.5ins
TL 520243	Hawthorn	Pollard	2.12m	6ft 11.5ins
TL 523242	Tulip Tree	Standard	5.0m	16ft 5ins
TL 523241	Larch	Standard	3.20m	10ft 6.5ins
TL 523241	Redwood	Standard	4.19m	13ft 9ins
TL 523242	Black Mulberry	Pollard	2.52m	8ft 3ins

Elsenham Hall (Private)

TL 542258	Beech	Standard?	6.02m	19ft 9ins

(For Hylands Park see chapter on Veteran Trees and Saproxylic Invertebrates)

The Birds of Essex Parks

Parks have made a major contribution to the history of bird recording in Essex. There is now a substantial, but dispersed body of information in publications, such as the county avifaunas – Christy (1890), Glegg (1929) and Cox (1984) and the Essex Bird Report concerning the birds of Essex parks.

Most of the very early park records, for example those in Christy's Birds of Essex (1890) sadly refer to birds that were shot. Many parks up to 1914 were heavily keepered and raptors and corvids particularly were strictly controlled – being regarded as vermin. It seems also that very few rare birds escaped the gun in the nineteenth century – the Victorian mania for collecting things natural ensured that rarities ended-up under glass domes in parlours, or the glazed cases of serious collectors and museums. Taxidermy was considered very fashionable in Victorian Britain and many towns and villages had their resident taxidermist. Notable Essex taxidermists included Doubleday of Epping, Pettitt of Colchester and Travis of Saffron Walden. The introduction of Becoeur's arsenical soap (as a preservative) early in the 19th century and the Great Exhibition of 1851, were two key events providing impetus to the collecting of birds.

One of the earliest collections of stuffed birds in Essex was formed by the fourth Lord Braybrooke (1820 – 1861) at Audley End near Saffron Walden. The collection was also added to by the fifth Lord. The cases were originally displayed in the Picture and Lower Galleries, removed in the 1940s when such things were considered to be in poor taste, but reinstated in the 1980s as a remarkable survival and typical of the Victorian period by English Heritage. The extensive collection consisted of over a hundred cases of British, European and exotic birds. Importantly, from the point of view of this publication, most of the early specimens of British birds were those shot at Audley End or on neighbouring estates. Some of those recorded by Christy are listed below.

Some of the Uncommon Birds recorded at Audley End in the 19th Century:

Bewick's Swan (1841)	Pied Flycatcher (1881)
Bittern (1831)	Raven (n.d.)
Black-necked Grebe (1838)	Red-breasted Merganser (1850)
Black Tern (1836)	Scaup (1830)
Crossbill (1836)	Short-eared Owl (1881)
Goosander (1838)	Slavonian Grebe (1838)
Hawfinch (1837 & 1858)	Smew (1838)
Honey Buzzard (1838)	Storm Petrel (1836)
Long-eared Owl (1834)	Whooper Swan (1838)
Merlin (1837 & 1853)	Wood Warbler (c.1845)

The winter of 1837 – 38 was very severe and this probably accounts for the presence of some birds on this list.

Parks, as well as providing wood-pasture habitat, often had substantial areas of open water. Chapman & Andre (1777) show lakes in a number of Essex parks – the largest being those at Gosfield, Debden Hall, Navestock and Wanstead (the latter were extant in the 17th century). New Hall, Boreham, is also shown with a huge "pond" adjacent to the park. In the pre-Lea Valley/Abberton/Hanningfield days, these park lakes were the only source of sizeable open water in inland Essex and obviously attracted many notable wildfowl.

The wood-pasture aspect of Essex parks seems to have attracted a particular group of birds. The fourteen species listed below regularly feature in records from Essex Parks (all dates included):

Great Spotted Woodpecker	Redstart
Green Woodpecker	Spotted Flycatcher
Hawfinch	Stock Dove
Jackdaw	Tawny Owl
Lesser Spotted Woodpecker	Treecreeper
Nightingale	Tree Pipit
Nuthatch	Wood Warbler

Crossbills, probably since the introduction of many Conifers to Essex parks since the 19th century, are also notable. Two surprising results from the literature search were the number of Ravens recorded (some breeding) in Essex parks in the 19th century (it is now extinct in the county) and the lack of specific records of Wryneck from Essex parks – it has been stated to be a parkland species, but most of the records I have come across seem to be from large gardens. Tree Sparrow and Red-backed Shrike also do not seem to figure highly in park records.

An arbitrary selection of some of the rarer birds is given below, along with a list of seven of the typical parkland species, together with the parks they were recorded at. Lastly, a list of a few of the many escaped exotics that have turned-up in Essex parks is included. The bird list in Section II Hylands Park gives a good indication of the more regularly recorded Essex parkland species.

References:

Christy, R.M. (1890) *The Birds of Essex*. Essex Field Club.

Cox, S.(1984) *A new Guide to the Birds of Essex*. (EBWPS).

Glegg, W.E. (1929) *A History of the Birds of Essex*. London.

Taylor, M.P. (1965) The Bird Life of Weald Park (1962 – 1965) in *Essex Bird Report* 1965 p. 51 – 55 (EBWPS)

Uncommon Birds – A selection from Essex Parks

Bee-eater	Thorndon (1979)
Bittern	Lawford Hall (1901) Marks Hall (1885)
Black-necked Grebe	Debden Park (1881) Wanstead Park (1981)
Black Tern	Wanstead Park (1926)
Common Buzzard	Shortgrove (1881) Gilwell Park (1924)
Corn Bunting	Thorndon (1978) Dagnam Park (1962)

Gadwall	Shortgrove (1862) Navestock (1920)
Golden Eagle	Easton Park (probable) (1877)
Goldeneye	Shortgrove (1830) Wanstead Park (1982)
Golden Oriole	Lawford Hall (1830) Thorndon Park (1975) Dagnam Park (1987)
Goosander	Debden Park (1830) Wanstead Park (1885)
Great Grey Shrike	Shortgrove (1854) Marks Hall (1974)
Grey Phalarope	Wanstead Park (1875 and 1963)
Hobby	Hill Hall (>1847) Hylands (2001 – 02) Wanstead Park (1991)
Honey Buzzard	Wivenhoe Park (1867) Copford Hall (1927)
Hooded Crow	Gosfield Park (1927) Weald Park (1965)
Hoopoe	Braxted Park (c.1850) Langford Park (c.1886) Wanstead Park (1976)
Nightjar	Gilwell Park (1926) Thorndon (1956) Wanstead Park (1892) Ongar Park Wood (1969)
Osprey	Debden Park (1817) Gosfield Park (1908) Weald Park (1903)
Pied Flycatcher	Wanstead Park (1983) Bedfords Park (1958) Dagnam Park (1993)
Pintail	Navestock Park (1920) Weald Park (1910)
Raven	Audley End (mid-19th century) Copped Hall (1846) Debden Park (mid-19th century)

Raven (cont.)	Latton Park (1920) Lawford Hall (1870 – 80) Wanstead Park (1833/4) Warden's Hall (to 1865)
Red-backed Shrike	Thorndon (1959) Littley Park (1927 – 28)
Red-breasted Flycatcher	Wanstead Park (1968)
Red-breasted Merganser	Debden Park (1837)
Red Kite	Leez Priory (<1768)
Red-necked Grebe	Wanstead Park (1877) Debden Park (1839)
Red-necked Phalarope	Debden Park (1881)
Red-rumped Swallow Red-throated Diver	Wanstead Park (1975) Debden Park (n.d.) Wanstead Park (1877)
Ring Ouzel	Dagnam Park (1984) Weald Park (1984)
Roller	Great Chesterford Park (1865)
Rough-legged Buzzard	Shortgrove (1839)
Snow Goose	Barrington Hall (1921)
Spotted Redshank	Little Chesterford Park (1887)
Tree Sparrow	Thorndon (1975) (150+) Weald Park (1997)
Turnstone	Navestock Park (1912)
Water Rail	Gosfield Park (1922) Shortgrove (1955)
Waxwing	Thorndon (1972)
White-tailed Eagle	Weald Park (1909) Navestock Park (1928)
Woodlark	Thorndon (c.1950) Dagnam Park (1994) Weald (1997)

Note: Great White Egret (Heron) recorded from Lexden Park (1901) and European Hawk Owl recorded from Gibcracks, Danbury (1913) are not admitted to the current Essex List – the first on the grounds of incomplete evidence, the second on the grounds of suspected fraud.

Notable Parkland Species (all dates, some passage, as well as breeding)

Crossbill	Bedfords, Copped Hall, Latton, Thorndon, Weald, Wivenhoe, Writtle
Hawfinch	Audley End, Braxted, Copped Hall, Dagnam, Danbury, Hylands, Ongar Park Wood, Thorndon, Weald, Wanstead
Nightingale	Dagnam, Hylands, Marks Hall, Thorndon, Weald, Wivenhoe, Wanstead
Redstart	Dagnam, Danbury, Thorndon, Weald, Wanstead
Spotted Flycatcher	Audley End, Bedfords, Braxted, Copped Hall, Dagnam, Danbury, Havering, Hylands, Ongar Park Wood, Wanstead, Weald, Wivenhoe
Tree Pipit	Bedfords, Braxted, Copped Hall, Dagnam, Hylands, Marks Hall, Ongar Park Wood, Thorndon, Weald, Wanstead
Wood Warbler	Audley End, Dagnam, Danbury, Hylands, Thorndon, Wanstead, Weald

Exotic Escapes in Parks

Black Swan	Audley End (2000), Weald (2000)
Chiloe Wigeon	Weald (2001)
Emperor Goose	Weald (2000)
Guinea Fowl	Braxted (2003) (released)
Hooded Merganser	Copped Hall (2001)
Ring-necked Parakeet	Highams (1970s>), Wanstead (2001), Wivenhoe (2000)
Sulphur-crested Cockatoo	Thorndon (1997)

Wood-Pasture and Parks

It is only relatively recently that lowland wood-pasture as a habitat type has been recognised. It is, by its simplest definition, an area of land where the growing of trees was combined with the grazing of animals. Included under this definition are wooded commons, ancient royal forests, chases and parks. The trees within a wood-pasture are characteristically pollards – trees cut at a height which would prevent livestock from browsing the re-growth. Parks stocked with deer in the medieval period differed from forests, in having a deer-proof perimeter fence - the pale – were privately owned and were not governed by a legal system or special administration. Hylands came late to this group. It was created in the early 18th century from a pre-existing agricultural landscape, as were many much earlier parks. Characteristically Hylands was surrounded by an oak pale; animals including cattle and sheep were grazed here and today a large herd of fallow deer (around a hundred head) roam the park, although the perimeter fence is no longer deer-proof. Pollard trees are present in the park, albeit in small numbers (and all are of hedgerow origin). As a park created for its visual amenity, rather than as a producer of venison, standard trees – including a number of sizeable oaks – are in the majority.

Hylands is not of medieval origin, although it does incorporate elements of ancient landscapes within its current boundary. The Great Oak on Writtle Hills – possibly more than 500 years old – probably started life in the 15th or 16th century. Hylands is relatively young, at about 270 years old (in part). Parks such as this are sometimes termed 'pseudo-medieval', but there is no real justification for this term, since many medieval parks were created in this way as well and we don't refer to medieval parks as being 'pseudo-Saxon'. In 1320 Edward I gave leave "to inclose 150 acres of demesne adjoining park of Waltham and High Easter called Le Plessie to enlarge that Park". The resulting enlarged Pleshey Great Park, comprising some 625 acres of coppiced woodland, hedgerows, trees and pasture, is little different in structure to the 570 acres of Hylands Park today.

Even now, what is Britain's best studied deer park – Moccas Park in Herefordshire – (famous for its rare beetles and now a national nature reserve) may not be medieval in origin. There appears to be no record of a licence to empark (possibly one was not applied for) and the park is first recorded in the early 17th century. In 1617 some deer were sent from Moccas to stock a park in Ireland. The Lower Park at Moccas has ridge and furrow (probably medieval) and according to John Phibbs – "Most of the veteran oaks stand on the ridge and furrow". Its most famous tree – the "Hypebaeus Tree" (named for a rare beetle only known in Britain from Moccas) – a very ancient oak pollard "appears to be in origin, a hedgerow tree". So Moccas in fact may be a 'pseudo-medieval' park created in part out of agricultural land that had gone out of cultivation much earlier, possibly during the 'Black Death'.

The vast Richmond Park in Surrey, twice the size of Hatfield Forest and another National Nature Reserve, was emparked as late as 1637 by Charles I as a place to hunt red deer – hence its size. It too consisted of existing farmland, but also common land and woodland (relatively little Crown land was involved in its creation).

Parks have been created virtually throughout England's history since the Conquest and still goes on today in the form of 'country parks', which are emparked for their wild-life and public amenity, not for their deer. At all times there has been an ebb and flow of park creation – thousands were made in the medieval period, hundreds disparked in the 17th and 18th centuries. A feature of Essex parks is that they were created and adapted from a pre-existing, sometimes agricultural, landscape of woodland, fields and pastures.

Wood-pasture in Essex today

It is enormously difficult to give an assessment of the actual acreage of wood-pasture in Essex today. There is only a small amount of working wood-pasture, ie where animals are grazed beneath actively pollarded trees, as at Hatfield Forest. There is slightly more where animals are grazed, but the trees are not managed as at Weald Park. Assessment is complicated by some sites, such as Hylands, which has no formal grazing regime, but the park is mown (grass and for hay) and is also accessed by a substantial herd of fallow deer. Some very old parks which are now disparked and are largely arable fields, can still have relict areas of wood-pasture. It is still possible to see cattle grazing on old pasture beneath old ash pollards at what was Littley Park near Hartford End.

The wood-pasture total below includes all these categories, including derelict wood-pasture in which no grazing or wood-cutting takes place at all. It also takes into account private wood-pasture sites, which may or may not be working. The total acreage of parks does not include many small parks (less than 40 acres) and of the estimated total of 4,000 acres, a significant percentage of that acreage comes from just eight parks, including Hylands (577), Thorndon (435), Weald (425), Braxted, Dagnam, Shortgrove, Stansted Hall and St Osyth. Hylands, at 577 acres, is by my calculation the largest park in Essex today. Essex, with sites such as Epping and Hatfield Forests (totalling some 7,000 acres) and parks, including Weald, Thorndon, Quendon, Stansted Hall, Langleys, Hassobury, Barrington Hall and St Osyth - which all have grazing animals – may make a very significant contribution to Britain's acreage of lowland wood-pasture.

Total wood-pasture in Essex today

	Acres	Hectares
Forests (Epping, Hatfield and Hainault)	7,360	2,981
Parks (estimated)	4,000	1,618
Wooded Commons	255	103
Total:	**11,615**	**4,700**

 Harvey in 2002, writing in his book 'Parkland', suggests there may be as little as 74,130 acres (30,000 hectares) of lowland wood-pasture in Britain, which considering there were probably 40,000 acres (16,188 hectares) of medieval park in Essex alone (not including forests and wooded commons) is a substantial decline of a very important biotope.

Essex Parks – location and access

The list below includes existing parks and the sites of some that have been disparked. Included are just 66 of the over 160 parks that have existed in Essex. Only some 25% of those listed have formal public access (bold), the rest are private and their owners privacy should be respected; for these, access is by permission only. However, many Essex parks are traversed by footpaths (see relevant O.S. Map) and it is still possible to get the 'feel' of many parks by this route. Public parks currently with free access include Bedfords, Belhus, Dagnam, Danbury, Gaynes (Upminster) now Parklands, Havering, Hylands, Mistley, Thorndon, Wanstead and Weald. Access to the grounds of Audley End and Marks Hall are by payment of a fee. Some parks may levy a car-parking fee. Some historic buildings either in, or formerly in or adjacent to a parkland setting, such as Audley End, Blake Hall, Castle Hedingham, Hylands and Ingatestone Hall, are open (or partly open) to the public. Chalkney Wood and Norsey Wood (formerly a swine park and deer park respectively) are both public access, but have not been included on the list.

Note: The grid reference is usually centred on the park or historic building. It does not indicate public access.

Absol	TL 665194	**Hylands**	**TL 683043**
Albyns	TQ 508968	Ingatestone	TL 653986
Alresford	TM 070200	Kelvedon Hall	TL 558004
Audley End	**TL 524383**	Langleys	TL 700137
Barrington Hall	TL 548173	Lawford	TM 085315
Bedfords	**TQ 520922**	Lexden	TL 972248
Belhus	**TQ 573813**	Littley	TL 695175
Blake Hall	TL 537053	**Marks Hall**	**TL 841259**
Boreham	TL 746093	Messing	TL 893183
Braxted	TL 856155	**Mistley**	**TM 116313**
Castle Hedingham	TL 786344	Navestock Hall	TQ 540987
Claybury Hall	TQ 430913	New Hall	TL 733105
Copped Hall	TL 430016	Ongar	TL 500023
Crondon	TL 692005	Pleshey Great	TL 658170
Dagnam	**TQ 550930**	Pond	TL 695191
Danbury	**TL 770051**	Pyrgo	TQ 523939
Donyland (E)	TM 023210	Quendon	TL 517315
Donyland (W)	TL 995205	Rayleigh	TQ 824898
Down Hall	TL 523132	Rivenhall	TL 816190
Easton Lodge	TL 593240	St Osyth	TM 120160
Fairmead	**TQ 398947**	Shortgrove	TL 525355
Gaynes (Theydon)	TL 485016	Skreens	TL 626080
Gaynes (Upminster)	**TQ 559852**	Stansted Hall	TL 522245
Gidea	TQ 526903	Terling	TL 773146
Gilwell	TQ 385965	**Thorndon**	**TQ 615913**
Gosfield	TL 772298	Thundersley	TQ 792883
Hadleigh	TQ 813863	Waltham	TQ 388018
Hallingbury	TL 520190	**Wanstead**	**TQ 417875**
Harolds	TL 413045	Warlies	TL 417013
Hassobury	TL 483250	**Weald**	**TQ 573944**
Hatfield	TL 555205	**West Ham**	**TQ 400843**
Havering	**TQ 497928**	Wivenhoe	TM 032240
Hill Hall	TQ487995	Writtle	TL 653033

Glossary of Park Terms

Aper - boar

Arcus – bow

Averria - mentioned in 1229 in Havering Park, the term seems to refer to domestic rather than wild swine, both of which are recorded in the park at this time

Avesagium – payment for pannage

Ballista – crossbow

Bank and ditch - parks often had a boundary bank with an internal ditch to keep animals in. Sometimes a significant earth-work as at Ongar Great Park, in other cases, as in the Tudor Fairmead Park, no trace of a boundary bank and ditch can be found. The bank was usually surmounted with the park pale (see fossatum)

Battue - The hue and cry that drove the deer from their enclosure, the paroke, towards the hunting party in a Tudor ritual hunt

Berner – **(also Bernarius)** - keeper of dogs

Bovettus – **(also bouettis)** - a young ox

Brake - brake fern or bracken (*Pteridium aquilinum*), rarely recorded in park literature. It was usually collected in the autumn for animal litter and for covering root vegetables to keep the frost off. Its main use for deer was as cover for the fawns. In 1331 – 2 bracken was sold from Rayleigh Park

Brocket – young male red deer

Browse - branches cut from pollards as a supplementary feed for the deer

Buck - a mature male fallow deer

Buckhay - an enclosure for holding deer (see also deerhay)

Buckstall - a device for trapping deer

Cablicium - fallen wood

Capreolus – roebuck

Clap-gate - a self-closing swing-gate that prevented deer and other livestock from straying from a park. Clap-gate Lane at Waltham Abbey possibly commemorates such a gate on the northern edge of Waltham Park

Compartment - an enclosed area within a park, often with a boundary bank with an external ditch (to keep animals out). Coppiced woodland is the usual reason for a permanent enclosure. Temporary enclosures (fenced) could be made to separate livestock

Crotties - deer droppings

Deer - the introduction of deer, most often fallow, but sometimes red in Essex, sometimes the gift of the King, marked the establishment of the deer park.

Deerbank - the deerbank at Norsey Wood, Billericay, is possibly the boundary bank of a former deer park phase in the wood's history; the wood is mentioned as a park in 1323

Deer cage - a cart with a wooden cage for transporting live deer. Deer were often transported long distances – from Havering to Flanders in 1238, from Thorndon to New Zealand in the 19th century

Deer coursing - the coursing of deer by greyhounds is mentioned up to the 18th century, possibly a development from the Tudor ritual hunt

Deer-creep - deer are adept at getting through small gaps. A creep is a place, for example under a deer-proof fence, where deer squeeze through

Deer hay - a fenced or hedged enclosure for deer (ie a park). In Anglo-Saxon 'derhage', mentioned for Ongar Park

Deer-leap - a gap in a park pale with a low fence externally but with a significant drop internally, so that deer could enter the park, but could not get out

Dispark - the act of terminating the existence of a park, usually involving the removal of the deer and the pale and the eventual sale of the land

Doe - female fallow deer

Dolia - casks for transporting live fish

Dotardes - (also dotrells, dodderel and dry oaks) - old trees, often old pollards, fit only for firewood (and rare beetles)

Dove-cote - (also Columbarium) - a building for keeping doves in

Empale - (also impale) – the act of fencing the park

Empark - (also impark) – the act of creating a park which required a licence from the Crown, a park pale and the introduction of deer

Excaetis - (also escaeta) - wood cut from a felled tree (see also lops and tops)

Fallow deer – Fallow (*Dama dama*), the favoured deer for the medieval deer park

Feuterer - the handler of a greyhound used for hunting or coursing

Ferarum - (feras) – collectively the King's beast or beasts, in practise applied to deer

Fodere - to dig. The King's swine in Havering Park were required to have rings in their noses to prevent them from rooting up the park

Foreign wood - boscus forinsecus, with reference to Havering Park, a wood outside the Park (and also Hainault Forest), but still within the manor

Fossatum - a ditch or bank (or both)

Freeboard - a strip of land around the perimeter of some parks, kept clear for inspection and repair of the park pale

Gate lodge - the main entrance gate to the park often had a lodge. In about 1531 John Glynne is mentioned as the Keeper of the Southgate at Havering Park. A gate-keepers' lodge is mentioned here in 1650

Greyhound - the favoured dog for pursuing the deer; a dog that hunts by sight. Also grewin (1550), a rarely used term

Ha-ha – a device prevalent from the 18th century onwards, which prevented deer and livestock from entering the gardens surrounding mansions, but did not intrude into the view from the house, as a fence would

Hart - another name for a red deer stag, but could also be used for a fallow buck.

Hatch – (also Hacche) – a gate

Hind – female red deer

Hinnulus – fawn (Fallow) or calf (Red)

Hunting-tower – similar in function to the standing; the one at Audley End, demolished c.1770, was probably unique in Essex. It was built on an eminence overlooking the mansion from which a good view of a hunt's progress could be achieved

Laund - a grassy plain where deer, cattle and sheep could graze in the park

Limer – a hound that hunted by scent

Lodge – the building from which the day-to-day work of the park was undertaken. Most parks usually had one placed where the most extensive views of the park could be had. Even when disparked, the name – ie Lodge Farm or Park Lodge Field – can usually be the clue to the existence of the former deer park

Lops and tops – wood trimmed from felled trees

Mast – usually acorn, upon which the pigs (pannage) or deer fed in the autumn

Mastinus – mastiff

Mews – a place where hawks and falcons, used for hawking, were housed

Mort – the sounding of the huntsman's horn on the death of a deer

Officials – about 1531 a list of the park officials are given who were based at Havering Park, a large royal park. Most parks would not have had this number of employees

John Gray	-	Keeper of the out-woods
John Glynne	-	Keeper of the south gate and pale
William Crane	-	Keeper of the park
John Wheler	-	Keeper of the manor of Havering-atte-Bower and the parks of Langlemere and Stratfield Mortymer
John Celye	-	Paler

Pale – the fence, usually of cleft oak pales, surrounding a deer park. In 1609 the repair of Havering's pale included work on the "posts, rails, pales and struts"

Paler - **(also palystere)** – one who made or repaired a park pale

Pannage – the foraging of pigs in autumn on the acorn crop

Parcus – in Domesday Book and later, a park

Park – an area of ground often licensed by the Crown and surrounded by a pale expressly for keeping deer or other beasts. Later applied to landscape parks which may not have had deer, just domestic stock and today to country parks – some of which (ie those on coastal grasslands) may never have seen a deer at all. Once disparked, the name often remaining, ie Park Farm or New Park Field, giving a clue to a park's possible previous existence

Parker – **(also parcarius)** - one who oversees a park; also the origin of the surname

Paroke – **(also perookez and peroke)** – a fenced enclosure within a park from where a Tudor ritual hunt would be conducted. Also later apparently used for deer coursing

Patte d'oie – literally goose foot, a series of rides radiating from a central point

Pillow-mound – artificial mound in a warren created for rabbits to burrow into

Pollard – a tree cut at 6 – 10ft above ground level to prevent livestock from browsing the re-growth. They produced firewood and other items, such as rails and hedging stakes and depending on the species, browst for the deer

Pricket – a 2nd year male fallow deer

Pynguedo – season of high grease (fatness) for venison

Quicksett – Hawthorn and Blackthorn for hedging parks

Red deer – the second favoured deer species for parks, requiring much larger parks than fallow. At Hedingham Castle, the Little Park or New Park was created specifically for red deer

Robora – **(also robur)** – usually taken to be an old pollard fit only for firewood (and rare beetles)

Sagitta – arrow

Salting house – mentioned for Havering Park in 1228. Presumably with the often large number of carcases to be dealt with, this building was constructed to process them

Saltory – a deer-leap (see back)

Slot – a deer's foot-print

Sorel – **(later sore)** – a young male fallow deer

Staddle – tree left in cleared woodland, or left to grow on when the rest of the coppice has been cut

Stag – a male red deer

Standing – an observation tower from which a ritual hunt could be viewed, as in Queen Elizabeth's Hunting Lodge. Probably also built in other parks as a raised observation platform to oversee the park

Stew pond – **(also stank)** – retaining pond for holding fish until required for the table

Teazer – smaller dog used to flush-out game or drive deer forward for the greyhounds to pursue

Tiercel – **(also Tercel or Tassel)** – a male falcon or hawk; a 'tercel gentle' was a male peregrine falcon

Timber – some parks, such as Havering, were important suppliers of structural timber for building. Timber from Havering went to the Tower of London, old St Paul's Cathedral and possibly even into the great hall of Westminster Palace

Toils – heavy-duty nets used to catch deer alive, either for subsequent slaughter or for transporting alive to another park

Underwood – coppiced woodland, compartmented in a deer park and protected from browsing animals by a ditch and bank with a fence or hedge

Vadletti – generic term for huntsmen, it was strictly speaking a term for varlets, as opposed to the senior huntsmen in the royal hunting establishment's hierarchy

Wall – because of the expense, parks were rarely walled. Exceptions include Richmond Park, with several miles of wall and in Essex, Audley End, Braxted and Hylands (partly)

Warren – an area specifically for rearing rabbits

Water-gate – mentioned for Havering Park in 1609; presumably a gate that allowed the parker to regulate the water level in ponds or lakes

Wild-swine – **(also wild boar)** – another royal beast, largely extinct in the wild by the 15th century, but kept on in some parks; in Havering and also Chalkney Wood, in the latter up to the 1520s – 1530s

Wood-pasture – **(also silva-pastilis)** – a land-use type characteristic of the medieval period and in its simplest form, where the grazing of animals was combined with the production of wood and timber. Broadly covering ancient royal Forests, chases, wooded commons and parks

Wyppys – one of a number of diseases that afflicted deer in the medieval period. Others included garget, rotte and murrayn

Bibliography and References

Abraham, E. (1988) Hylands – an architectural history. Chelmsford Borough Council

Addison, W. (1949) Essex Heyday. Dent

Anon – (2002) A Hunting Lodge at Stansted. Essex Past and Present. November p.14

Braybrooke, Lord (1836) The History of Audley End (Samuel Bentley, London)

Briggs, N. (1989) Georgian Essex. E.R.O.

Cantor, L. (1983) The Medieval Parks of England (Loughborough University of Technology)

Cassidy, R. (1978) A Short History of Copped Hall. Upshire Pres. Soc. & Waltham Abbey Historical Society

Cassidy, R. (1983) Copped Hall – a short history. Waltham Abbey Historical Society (Reprinted 1985)

Conway, H. (1996) Public Parks. Shire Garden History No. 9

Cowell, F. (1986 – 87) Richard Woods (?1716 – 93) A Preliminary Account. Parts I, II & III. Garden History. (p.19 – 54, 85 – 119 & 115 – 135)

Cowell, F. & Green,G. (eds.) (2000) A Gazetteer of Sites in Essex associated with Humphry Repton. Essex Gardens Trust

Daniel, W.B. (1812) Rural Sports Vol. 1. London

Dobson, J. (1999) The Mammals of Essex. Lopinga Books

Drury, P.J. & Gow,J.R. (1984) Audley End. H.M.S.O.

Emmison, F.G. (1961) Tudor Secretary – Sir William Petre at Court and Home. Longmans

Emmison, F.G. (1970) Elizabethan Life : Disorder. Essex County Council

English Heritage (1987) Register of Parks and Gardens of Historic Interest. Part 15, Essex (with later revisions)

Fisher, J.L. (1997) A Medieval Farming Glossary of Latin and English Words (2nd edition revised by A. & R. Powell reprint 2003) E.R.O.

Foreman, S. (1999) Hylands – the story of an Essex Country House and its owners. Ian Henry Publications. 2nd edition

Fowkes, R.L. and Ramsey, W.G. (1986) Epping Forest – then and now. Plaistow Press

Green, L.S. (ed.) (1999) The Essex Landscape. In search of its history. Essex County Council

Gunton, T. (2000) Wild Essex. Lopinga Books

Harding, P.T. & Wall,T. (2000) Moccas: an English deer park. English Nature

Harvey, G. (2002) Parkland. National Trust – Living Landscapes

Hunter, J.M. (1994) Medieval and Tudor Parks of the Middle Chelmer Valley. Essex Archaeology and History 25, P113 – 118

Hunter, J.M. (1994) Littley Park, Great Waltham – historical survey. Essex Archaeology and History 25 p.119 – 124

Hunter, J.M. (1999) The Essex Landscape – a study of its form and history. E.R.O.

Jarvis, L.Donald (1991) Crondon Parke in ye Hamlet of Orset. Essex Journal Vol. 26 No. 2.

Jones, P.Fletcher (1972) Richmond Park – Portrait of a Royal Playground. Phillimore

Lasdun, S. (1992) The English Park. Royal, public and private. The Vendome Press

Laver, H. (1898) The Mammals, Reptiles and Fishes of Essex. Essex Field Club Special Memoir No. III

Mason, S. (1990) Essex on the Map. E.R.O.

Morant, P. (1768) The History and Antiquities of the County of Essex. Vols I & II. London

Pepper, S. et al (1977) Weald Country Park. Essex County Council

Pepper, S. et al (1979) Thorndon Country Park. Essex County Council 2nd reprint

Plumptre, G. (1993) The Garden Makers. Pavilion

Pusey, R. (1985) A Discovery of Old Essex. Hale

Rackham, O. (1976) Trees and Woodland in the British Landscape. Dent

Rackham, O. (1980) Ancient Woodland – its history, vegetation and uses in England. Arnold

Rackham, O. (1986) The History of the Countryside. Dent

Rackham, O. (1986) The Woods of South-east Essex. Rochford District Council

Rackham, O. (1989) The Last Forest – the story of Hatfield Forest. Dent

Rackham, O. (1992) Lodges and Standings in Hanson,M.W.(ed.) Epping Forest – through the eye of the Naturalist. Essex Field Club

Reaney, P.H. (1935) The Place-names of Essex. English Place-name Society Vol. XII

Ryan, P.M. (1994) A History of Marks Hall (Thomas Phillips Price Trust)

Seddon, J. (2003) Queen Elizabeth's Hunting Lodge – a brief history (Corporation of London)

Shirley, E.P. (1867). English Deer Parks. John Murray.

Smith, D. (1931) Pigeon Cotes and Dove Houses of Essex. (Clarke & Co.)

Smith, H. (1925) A History of the parish of Havering-atte-Bower, Essex. Benham & Co. (reprint London Borough of Havering 1990)

Watkin, B. (1994) The buildings of Littley Park. Essex Archaeology and History 25. p125 – 133

Young, A. (1807) General View of the Agriculture of the County of Essex (Vols I & II)

Introduction

M.W.Hanson

The second part of this book is devoted to the results of a three year (2000 – 2003) survey by the Essex Field Club of Hylands Park, Chelmsford. The park is owned and managed by Chelmsford Borough Council. The survey sought to record all aspects of the park's natural history from mosses and lichens to flies, birds and beetles. A preliminary aim was to record and assess those species of conservation value found within the park. Because of the wood-pasture nature of the site, an assessment of the saproxylic invertebrate fauna was thought to be a priority.

The survey was important for a number of reasons – as far as I am aware, it is the first time a 'full' survey of an Essex park has been undertaken with the results being published. Many other wood-pasture sites in Britain – for example, the New Forest, Windsor Forest and Moccas Park – have for decades been famous for their rare saproxylic beetles. Hylands was a relatively unstudied and little known site. Hylands is also obviously not in the 'Premiership' league of sites, such as Windsor Great Park, Richmond Park, or Moccas Park (in fact, it probably barely scrapes into Division I!) yet it still provides records of Red Data Book saproxylics such as the hoverfly *Callicera spinolae*, which have yet to be recorded from more famous sites.

Hylands is also important, probably as much for what has not been recorded here as for what has. Being a park created in the 18th and 19th centuries out of existing meadow, pasture, coppiced woodland and a few pre-existing ancient trees, later augmented with numerous ornamental plantings, the species lists should make a useful comparison with lists from earlier medieval, Tudor and Stuart parks elsewhere.

The survey also highlights our general lack of knowledge of the wildlife of Essex parks. Hylands has produced records of 59 nationally notable or Red Data Book invertebrates. I suspect that many other Essex parks could surpass this total and would make an even more significant contribution to nature conservation in Essex than Hylands.

One aspect of looking into the wildlife of Hylands Park is how contemporary much of the biological recording is. Some twelve years ago I published a book about Epping Forest and this involved researching an immense amount of historical material from a very wide range of sources. With Hylands this aspect has been (pleasantly!) largely absent.

It would take many lifetimes and the co-operation of numerous owners to achieve a comprehensive list of the wildlife of all Essex parks, but I hope this section on Hylands will give at least a flavour of what could be expected to occur in other Essex parks.

Hylands Park – A Brief History

M.W.Hanson

It is certain that at least some of the Hylands Park we see today formed part of, and was within the legal boundary of, the ancient Royal Forest of Writtle.

A perambulation of Writtle Forest made on the 6 – 8th November 1358, copied into the 1566 survey of the Petre estates (ERO: D/DPM1325) and translated by Oliver Rackham , reads (in part):

"and thus thence going by the said way up to a certain Cross called Widforde
Crosse,
which Cross stands at the end of a certain lane which leads to the Toft
formerly of Henry Genett,
and thus thence by a certain ditch called Holeweldiche up to the land lately of
Walter de Bruys and now belonging to the Manor of Widford;
and thus by a certain descent to the bridge called Widforde Bridge,
and from that bridge by the same water up to the place where a water-Mill
called Widforde Mell lately was sited;
and from the place of that Mill by a certain Hedge called la Ley up to a certain
Field called Widforde ffrith which divides the townships of Writtell and
Widforde,
and thus thence to the Corner of the said Field *versus le east,*
and from that place up to the messuage formerly Ralph Wolsse's, and now
belonging to the heirs of John de Widforde, standing on the King's way
which leads from Chelmisforde towards London,
and thus always by that King's way to the land lately John Locksmythe's …
[*next day*] Beginning at the land of John Locksmyth next Shyngledecrouche in
Widforde,
going straight up to the Messuage lately William de Wellys's and now William
De Gibbe's,
and from that messuage by a certain lane to the house lately William
Roughey's and now John Hasell's,
and from that messuage by a certain hedge which divides the townships of
Writtell and Sowthwoodde."

The Widford Bridge mentioned is (presumably) one sited where the current bridge stands, where the old Roman road (London Road) crosses the Wid. It also mentions South Wood, confirming the wood is a true ancient woodland, probably well over 650 years old.

The land upon which Hylands has developed is mentioned as belonging to one Thomas Hawkins in a will dated 1500. One part was called Highlands Field and with other property – including a house called Hooks – was left to the church; the entire income from the bequest was to be used by the vicar of Writtle. Ironically, the site and remains of Hooks still survive within the current boundary of Hylands. Hylands House itself was built around 1728 – 30 by wealthy lawyer Sir John Comyns, later Chief Baron of the Exchequer. A small park was created around the 1730 house, covering about 100 acres, including pasture, coppiced woodland and standard trees. A formal geometric garden was laid-out to the east of the house and a pleasure garden created north of the house. The Chapman and André map of 1777 clearly shows a small, but established, wood-pasture park surrounded by a park pale. The entire estate – put-up for sale in 1795 by the third John Comyns to own Hylands – included the park and 400 acres of adjacent farmland (Shackstones and Bridge Farms).

The estate was subsequently bought by Cornelius Kortright, a wealthy owner of estates in the West Indies in 1797. It was Kortright who promptly engaged the services of Humphry Repton, the landscape gardener, to produce a plan – in the form of a Red Book – for Hylands. Kortright also significantly enlarged the 1730 park, doubling its acreage to 213 acres (86 ha.).

At Hylands Repton's probable design (his Red Book is now lost) would have included the removal of the direct approach, the formal gardens and turn-around. The proposals probably also advocated a re-aligned approach to the house, the construction of a serpentine lake, a walled kitchen garden and shrubbery laid-out to the north-west with a ha-ha and clumps and belts of trees planted on the periphery of the park. Repton is also thought to have influenced the appearance of the house by designing the east and west wings and portico.

In July 2002 a team of archaeologists from the Museum of London were commissioned to look for, amongst other things, evidence of Repton's ha-ha located north of the house. A subsequent geophysical survey along the present-day fence line of the formal gardens failed to reveal any evidence of its existence. This is not surprising, since this was not the boundary c.1800. It is quite clear from the Michael John Mason estate map of 1814, that the ha-ha, if it did exist, would actually be very close to the house itself (at most, probably only 80 or 90 feet due north of the house). The north lawn was "replaced" in the 1990s. I have been told that it was ploughed before turf was laid and this would have removed any surface evidence of a filled-in ha-ha. I did notice, however, when a cable trench was dug across the back lawn, a brick rubble, slate and clay infill (to a depth of about 3ft) in what would be an appropriate position for the ha-ha. It would be a useful exercise to re-survey the north lawn area in order to confirm or deny the hypothesis that Repton's ha-ha in fact actually existed, mainly for reasons of historical accuracy.

Kortright resided at Hylands until 1814, when once again the estate was put-up for sale, eventually being purchased by the wealthy banker Pierre Caesar Labouchere. Labouchere employed the architect William Atkinson, who probably constructed several buildings in the park – at this time a new stable block and probably the home farm were built and a large walled kitchen garden was erected by the London Road main gate. A huge hot-house was constructed in the gardens, also possibly the work of Atkinson. Atkinson is also notable for his netted cherry orchard, created at Hylands in 1821.

Labouchere's death in 1839 caused the estate once again to be put on the market – the sales particulars mention the park and estate being enclosed with "oak park paling, a considerable portion new within the last year". An article in the Chelmsford Chronicle of 19th July 1839 gives the last known record of Repton's 'Red Book' for Hylands showing 'the former and present appearance of the house and grounds'.

John Attwood – industrialist and erstwhile M.P. for Harwich – bought Hylands and between 1842 and 1845 he commissioned the architect J.B.Papworth to alter the house and its interior decoration to his taste. The park was doubled in size from Labouchere's c.300 acres (120 ha.) to some 590 acres (239 ha.). The surrounding area was considerably altered by the acquisition and subsequent demolition of buildings that either intruded upon or interfered with his view from the park. This included Coptfold Hall, plus farms and other properties outside the park. I suspect that the property called Hooks, now within the boundary of the park, was also one of the properties that vanished. Attwood's zealous pursuit of privacy subsequently led to the closure of all the public roads across the park, including what had been the main Writtle to Ingatestone road and also the construction of a boundary wall along the eastern edge of the estate, separating the park from the London Road.

The late 19th century saw the demolition of the walled garden north of the house and the construction of three gate lodges. The kitchen garden, then of 8 acres (3.3 ha.), contained 16 houses devoted to fruit growing, including one for French beans and two for strawberries. An orchard was created west of the house. Arthur Pryor – owner of Hylands at this time – was a notable huntsman, shooting and riding to hounds over his considerable park and estate. A keen fisherman, he is also said to have attempted to introduce trout to Hylands Park.

The area of land covered by Hylands Park has varied enormously over time, dependent usually upon the financial situation of the owner. Much of the land sold was from the north part of the park, eventually being cultivated and then bought back by Chelmsford Borough Council.

The following table lists the acreage of the park at various dates:

DATE	ACRES	HECTARES	OWNER
1777	100 acres	40 ha.	John Comyns
1814	213 acres	86 ha.	Cornelius Kortright
1839	300 acres	212 ha.	Pierre Caesar Labouchere
1854	590 acres	239 ha.	John Attwood
1920	480 acres	194 ha.	Sir Daniel Fulthorpe Gooch
1962	433 acres	175 ha.	Christine Hanbury
2003	577 acres	234 ha.	Chelmsford Borough Council

Christine Hanbury, the last private owner of Hylands, enlarged the formal gardens and had the ha-ha south of the house built.

Chelmsford Borough Council have undertaken a phased restoration of the house (phase IV completed in 2003). There are also proposals to 'restore' the Repton landscape, for which Lottery funding has been granted.

References

Anon (2002) Discoveries at Hylands House, Essex Past & Present. November 2002 p.15.

Foreman,S. (1999) Hylands – the story of an Essex Country House and its owners. Ian Henry Publications (2nd Edition)

Hylands – notable dates

1728 – 30 Hylands built in red brick in the Queen Anne style. Park covers about 100 acres.

1738 Owner Sir John Comyns becomes Chief Baron of the Exchequer.

1745 John Comyns (II) takes-up residence.

1760 John Richard Comyns inherits.

1797 Cornelius Kortright purchases the estate.

1797 – 1803 Humphry Repton engaged to work on the park.

1814 Pierre Caesar Labouchere purchases the estate; park now 214 acres.

1819 – 25 William Atkinson engaged, probably working on a number of buildings in the park.

1839 Last known record of Repton's 'Red Book' for Hylands. John Attwood purchases estate.

c.1841 Wall built along London Road. Attwood buys-out public rights of way, including all roads, across park.

1858 Arthur Pryor purchases Hylands.

1882 Halt built on railway for the estate.

1907 Frederic Chancellor plan of Hylands House drawn-up.

1908 Sir Daniel Fulthorpe Gooch purchases Hylands.

1912 Famous 'aero-wedding' between Claude Graham-White and Dorothy Taylor.

1914 King George V visits Hylands.

1915 Lord Kitchener visits Hylands.

1922 John MacKenzie Hanbury purchases Hylands.

1920s Ha-Ha in front of house made.

1930s London Road dualized. Brick wall re-built inside former park boundary.

1940s Used as military command post inc. anti-aircraft division (T.A.). German P.O.W. camp established.

1944 Established as forward HQ for S.A.S.

1946 Essex Show held in park.

1962 Christine Hanbury, last private owner, dies.

1963 Fire in west wing of house.

1966 Park and house purchased by Chelmsford Borough Council for £150,000.

1967 South Wood Cottage demolished. Hylands House listed Grade II.

1971 A range of domestic utility buildings demolished between house and stable block.

1975 House upgraded to Grade II*.

1986 Restoration on house starts, porte cochere removed, replaced by early 19th century style portico. Construction of Chelmsford (A12) and Writtle (A414) by-passes.

1987 Ha-Ha rebuilt at cost of £14,100. Park and garden placed on English Heritage Register (now Grade II*). Great storm in October fells many trees.

1988 First 'Spectacular' held.

1993 Chelmsford Borough Council agrees to spend £3m in phased restoration.

1994 Phase I restoration starts.

1996 First 'V' Concert held. Archaeological dig in Kitchen Gardens.

2001 Western part of Brick Field drained.

2002 Phase IV restoration commences. New high voltage electricity cable laid across park. G.P.S. Mapping Survey of park. Archaeological surveys undertaken in formal gardens area, Flint Cottage and Repton's Approach.

2003 Heritage Lottery Funding granted to complete restoration of house, stable block and Repton landscape.

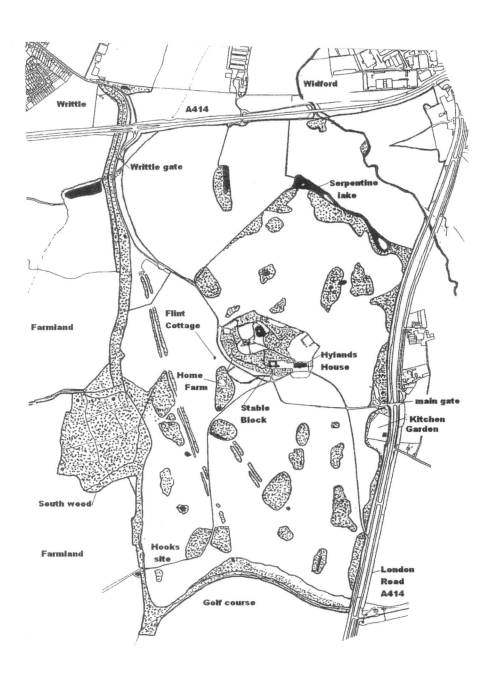

HYLANDS PARK

The Cultivated Landscape –
Hylands and its planted trees, shrubs and herbaceous plants

Mark Hanson

By the late 18th century, Hylands had established gardens, a sale catalogue of 1795 mentions "......a greenhouse, ice house, gardens and pleasure gardens........". Humphry Repton – commissioned by Cornelius Kortright around 1800 – is likely to have made a number of suggested alterations, amongst them creating a kitchen garden and a shrubbery to be laid out north-west of the house and removing the formal gardens.

In the 1820s, under the guidance of Pierre Labouchere, a huge 250ft greenhouse was built in the gardens and in 1821, a netted cherry orchard was created by the architect William Atkinson. In this structure cherries (May Duke, White Heart and Circasrain) and other soft fruit such as gooseberries, red, white and blackcurrants, raspberries and strawberries were grown. Labouchere also eventually had a new kitchen garden built in its current location by the main gate.

Labouchere employed two gardeners; Francis Nieman (fruit and vegetables) and John Smith (the flower and pleasure gardens) to supervise the gardens. Nieman, a Dutchman, employed the Dutch manner of forcing vegetables and fruit, substituting the heat of fermenting dung for that of coal. Thus, fresh vegetables were available virtually all year round – lettuces, cucumbers, carrots, kidney beans, cauliflowers, peas, potatoes, asparagus, sea kale and rhubarb. Herbs – such as chicory, parsley, mint and tarragon – were all grown in the kitchen garden. Exotic fruits that we take for granted now were also cultivated – melons, peaches, apricots, nectarines and grapes. Atkinson was a noted designer of greenhouses and using hot water for heating them. At least 16 glasshouses were constructed in the kitchen garden.

The hard winter of 1837 – 38 was reported on by J.A.Ferguson, Gardener at Hylands, and its effect on trees and shrubs. In the article published in the Gardeners Magazine are mentioned (amongst others) *Photinia serrulata, Magnolia grandiflora, Myrtus sp (Myrtle), Escallonia, Camellia, Arbutus, Aucuba, Viburnum tinus, Prunus laurocerasus, Rhododendron arboreum* and *Canna indica*. A deodar (*Cedrus deodara*) mentioned at 9ft high, unfortunately succumbed to the cold. This graceful conifer, a native of the Himalayas, was introduced into cultivation in 1831 and the tree concerned may have been one of the first grown in the U.K. Labouchere himself died not long after in 1839. A subsequent sales catalogue of this date mentions ".....magnificent conservatories and stove houses.....filled with a very choice collection of rare plants and exotics".

An article in the Gardeners Chronicle in June 1881 mentions Hylands Park as being "the largest gardening establishment in the neighbourhood of Chelmsford". (In 1839 Hylands was said to have employed some 30 gardeners and labourers). Plants noted here at this time included *Erysimum* (Belvoir Castle and Tom Thumb), *Aubrieta, Gloxinia* and *Calceolaria*. Special note was made of the *Bougainvillea*, today a common plant in the Mediterranean, but a native of Brazil. Two pine-houses are mentioned (for pineapples) and an Osborn's Prolific fig. Mention is made of the replanting of the trees trained on the walls. The recent orchard of four or five acres containing apples and also pears, notably had its trees protected from browsing cattle and rabbits.

Sir Daniel Fulthorpe Gooch, owner of Hylands 1908 – 1920 employed around 14 – 20 gardeners at Hylands. The vast greenhouse in the garden was by this time a palm, tropical and temperate house combined. However, this was not to continue and Christine Hanbury (the last private resident of Hylands from 1922 – 1962) reduced the greenhouse to a fraction of its original size and created a swimming pool within. Christine Hanbury also planted Rhododendron borders on the north lawn.

The year of 1966 saw Hylands taken-over by Chelmsford Borough Council. The 'Plant A Tree In 73' initiative saw some trees planted at Hylands, including apparently the Blue Atlantic Cedar in the formal gardens. A number of other trees have been planted to commemorate past mayors of Chelmsford and others 'in memoriam'. In 1978 some 2,000 trees were planted in the park with the suggestion that a further 8,000 were needed.

In April 1986 a proposed arboretum was announced, to be created in 34 acres of the park west of Home Farm and to consist of some 200 varieties of tree. The trees came from a number of sources, including Writtle College and also from Spains Hall, Nottcutts, Hilliers, Savill Garden, Royal Botanic Garden, Kew and Wakehurst Place. Unfortunately this joint venture between Writtle Agricultural College and Chelmsford Borough Council has not been deemed to be a success. A number of trees have died and the actual planting scheme is visually very unpleasing to the eye. Most of the trees are likely to be removed at some future date, but hopefully some of the more notable, well grown and aesthetically placed trees will be retained as a reminder of the arboretum's brief existence. Some trees, such as the Gean and Bird Cherry adjacent to Writtle Wood, are an important nectar source in spring for numerous insects. Others are well worth retaining because they are rare species in cultivation. (In November 2003 fourteen trees were transplanted to the grounds of Writtle College, mainly Ashes and Maples).

It is assumed that many of the modern plantations arose in the 1970s, such as Ash, Lightfoot and Poplar. Similarly, the London Road and Margaretting Belts arose at this time, presumably to replace the belts that had been lost to the dualization of the London Road in the 1930s, linear fragments of which remain in the central reservation of what is now the A414/London Road. Species planted in the 1970s included Oak, Ash, Beech, Hornbeam, Scots Pine and Hazel. The Writtle Belt is clearly much older; it is shown as an established entity on the 1878 Ordnance Survey Map.

The Tower Belt and Lower Belt are obviously of some age. The Tower Belt may be a fragment of a much larger ancient wood. The Lower Belt is also of some antiquity, but has had some plantings, including Horse Chestnut, Lime, Beech and Box. Box is present in several parts of the park, notably in South Wood, where some of them have reached tree size of around 20ft and also in Rook Plantation. This species and Snowberry are probably relics of the time when the park was an integral part of a 'sporting' estate. Lightfoot Spring, despite being very much 'ancient woodland' (with wild service, ramsons and bluebell) has also had some planting – most recently Beech and Hazel.

Hylands has three avenues of note – the oldest, The English Elm avenue, running from near what is now the Margaretting Gate towards Oak Plantation is defined by two rows of suckers – obviously the trees succumbed to Dutch Elm Disease in the late 1960s or 70s. It follows part of the course of what was the old road from London Road to Writtle and closed off by owner John Attwood in the 1840s. Roman Walk, an avenue of bundle-planted Common Hawthorn, cuts motorway-like across old field-boundaries and I suspect does not follow the course of any ancient trackway, but was called Roman Walk because of its straightness. It is probably an important and possibly unique landscape feature of Hylands Park dating from the 19th century. It also makes a significant contribution to the nectar resource of the park when it comes into flower in the spring.

The third avenue, of Horse Chestnut, is the most recent of the avenues and was planted within the ownership period of Chelmsford Borough Council. This avenue follows the access road from the main gate to the house. Assuming that it is retained (Repton did not like straight avenues of trees in his landscapes), it too will add significantly to the treescape of the park, will be an additional nectar source and ultimately, will provide good habitat for saproxylic invertebrates, particularly if pollarded.

The list of cultivated herbaceous plants are all species planted in the formal gardens, the vast majority in the period 2000 – 2003. The rose terrace (east of the house) was destroyed during building work in 2002, but re-made shortly afterwards and planted-up. Some remedial work around the collapsed wooden pergola during this period also resulted in some new plantings also included on the list. Over twenty varieties of Narcissus are to be found around the gardens and Home Farm (including the true Lent Lily, *Narcissus pseudo-narcissus*). The eight beds in the formal gardens host formal plantings (municipal type) in the winter and summer.

1. Cultivated Trees and Shrubs from Hylands Park
   (A = Arboretum F = Formal Gardens P = Park)

(Sandra Nicholson of Writtle College kindly provided details of plantings in the arboretum)

Abies koreana (A)

Abies veitchii (A)

Acer cappodocicum 'Aureum' (A)

Acer cappodocicum 'Rubrum' (A)

Acer davidii (A)

Acer lobelii (A)

Acer palmatum (F)

Acer platanoides (F)

Acer pseudo-platanus (F) (P)

Acer pseudo-platanus 'Atropurpureum' (P)

Acer rubrum (A)

Acer saccharinum (P)

Aesculus flava (P)

Aesculus hippocastanum (P)

Aesculus indica (A) (P)

Aesculus x *carnea* (P)

Aesculus x *carnea 'Plantierensis '* (A)

Alnus cordata (A) (P)

Alnus incana (A) (P)

Amelanchier (F)

Artemisia 'Powis Castle' (F)

Aucuba japonica 'variegata' (F)

Azalea 'Glowing Embers' (F)

Berberis thunbergii (F)

Betula humilis (A)

Betula jacquemontii (A)

Betula papyrifera (A)

Betula populifolia (A)

Buddleja davidii (F)

Buddleja globosa (F)

Buxus sempervirens 'Suffruticosa' (F)

Calocedrus decurrens (A)

Camellia japonica (F)

Carpinus betulus 'Incisa' (A)

Carpinus caroliniana (A)

Caryopteris x *clandonensis* 'Heavenly Blue' (F)

Castanea sativa (P)

Ceanothus thyrsiflorus var *repens* (F)

Cedrus atlantica (A)

Cedrus atlantica 'Glauca' Group (F)

Cedrus brevifolia (A)

Cedrus deodara (A) (F)

Celtis australis (A)

Celtis occidentalis (A)

Cercidiphyllum japonicum (A)

Cercis siliquastrum (A) (F)

Chaenomeles speciosa (F)

Chamaecyparis lawsoniana (F)

Cistus 'Silver Pink' (F)

Cotinus coggyria (F)

Cotoneaster (F)

Crataegus crus-galli (F)

Crataegus laevigata 'Paul's Scarlet' (P)

Crataegus prunifolia (A)

Crataegus x *lavallei* (A)

Daphne mezereum (F)

Deutzia x *hybrida* (F)

Escallonia (F)

Euonymus fortunei 'Emerald 'N' Gold' (F)

Euonymus fortunei 'Emerald Gaiety' (F)

Euonymus japonicus (F)

Euonymus japonicus 'Aureus' (F)

Fagus sylvatica Purpurea Group (F)

Fraxinus americana (A)

Fraxinus angustifolia (A)

Fraxinus angustifolia 'Raywood' (P)

Fraxinus chinensis subsp. *rhyncophylla* (A)

Fraxinus excelsior 'Diversifolia' (A)

Fraxinus excelsior 'Jaspidea' (A)

Fraxinus latifolia (A)

Fraxinus ornus (A)

Fraxinus pennsylvanica (A)

Fraxinus velutina (A)

Fuchsia (F)

Garrya elliptica (F)

Hebe (F)

Hibiscus syriacus (F)

Hydrangea macrophylla (F)

Hypericum calycinum (F)

Ilex aquifolium 'Argentea Marginata' (F)

Juglans nigra (A) (P)

Juglans regia (A) (P)

Laburnum (P)

Larix decidua (P)

Lavandula (F)

Lavatera thuringiaca (F)

Leycesteria formosa (F)

Ligustrum ovalifolium (P)

Liquidambar orientalis (A)

Liquidambar styraciflua (A) (F)

Lonicera fragrantissima (F)

Lonicera nitida (F)

Lonicera nitida 'Baggesen's Gold' (F)

Lonicera pileata (F)

Magnolia x *soulangeana* (F)

Mahonia aquifolium (F)

Mahonia x *media* 'Charity' (F)

Malus domestica (P)

Malus floribunda (A)

Malus sargentii (A)

Malus toringoides (A)

Mespilus germanica (A)

Nothofagus obliqua (A)

Ostrya carpinifolia (A)

Parrotia persica (A)

Philadelphus coronarius (F)

Phlomis (F)

Photinia x *fraseri* 'Red Robin' (F)

Picea abies (A)

Picea breweriana (A)

Picea omorika (A)

Pinus attenuata (A)

Pinus contorta (A)

Pinus leucodermis (A)

Pinus mugo (A)

Pinus nigra (A) (F) (P)

Pinus nigra subsp. *laricio* (A)

Pinus ponderosa (A)

Pinus strobus (A)

Pinus wallichiana (A)

Platanus orientalis (P)

Platanus x *hispanica* (P)

Podocarpus nivalis (A)

Populus balsamifera (A)

Populus nigra 'Italica' (A)

Populus trichocarpa (A)

Populus x *canadensis 'Eugenei'* (A)

Populus x *canadensis 'Robusta'* (A)

Populus x *candicans* (A)

Populus x *generosa* (A)

Potentilla fruticosa (F)

Prunus cerasifera (P)

Prunus laurocerasus (F) (P)

Prunus laurocerasus 'Magnoliifolia' (F) (P)

Prunus laurocerasus 'Marbled White' (F)

Prunus laurocerasus 'Otto Luykens' (F)

Prunus lusitanica (F) (P)

Prunus padus 'Watereri' (A)

Pseudostuga menziesii (P)

Pyracantha coccinea (F)

Pyrus domestica (P)

Quercus cerris (P)

Quercus frainetto (A)

Quercus ilex (P)

Quercus palustris (A) (F)

Quercus pyrenaica (P)

Quercus rubra (A) (F)

Quercus virginiana (A)

Rhododendron hybrids (F)

Rhododendron ponticum (F)

Ribes nigrum (P)

Ribes sanguineum (F)

Ribes uva-crispa (P)

Rosmarinus officinalis 'Frimley Blue' (F)

Rubus 'Benenden' (F)

Rubus tricolor (F)

Salix angularis (A)

Salix babylonica var. *pekinensis* (A)

Salix daphnoides 'Aglaia' (A)

Salix eleagnos (P)

Salix exigua (A)

Salix myrsinifolia (A)

Salix x *rubens 'Basfordiana'* (A)

Senecio greyi (F)

Sequoiadendron giganteum (A) (F)

Skimmia japonica (F)

Sorbus 'Joseph Rock' (A)

Sorbus aria (A) (P)

Sorbus commixta (A)

Sorbus hupehensis (A) (F)

Sorbus intermedia (A)

Spiraea japonica (F)

Symphoricarpos albus (F) (P)

Syringa vulgaris (F)

Taxus baccata 'Fastigiata' (F)

Tetradium danielli (A)

Thuja plicata (F)

Tilia dasystyla (A)

Tilia mongolica (A)

Tilia x *vulgaris* (P)

Ulmus 'Sapporo Autumn Gold' (A)

Ulmus x *hollandica* (P)

Viburnum opulus 'Roseum' (P)

Viburnum plicatum (F)

Viburnum rhytidophyllum (F)

Viburnum tinus (F)

Viburnum x *bodnantense* (F)

Weigela florida 'Variegata' (F)

Wisteria (F)

2. Native tree and shrub species planted at Hylands Park.

The following species have been recorded in the arboretum, formal gardens and plantations in the park.

Acer campestre	*Populus tremula*
Alnus glutinosa	*Prunus avium*
Betula pendula	*Prunus padus*
Betula pubescens	*Prunus spinosa*
Buxus sempervirens	*Pyrus pyraster*
Carpinus betulus	*Quercus petraea*
Castanea sativa	*Quercus robur*
Corylus avellana	*Salix alba*
Crataegus monogyna	*Salix cinerea*
Euonymus europaeus	*Salix pentandra*
Fagus sylvatica	*Sorbus aria*
Fraxinus excelsior	*Sorbus aucuparia*
Ilex aquifolium	*Taxus baccata*
Ligustrum vulgare	*Tilia cordata*
Malus sylvestris	*Tilia platyphyllos*
Pinus sylvestris	*Ulmus glabra*
Populus alba	*Ulmus minor*
Populus x *canescens*	*Ulmus procera*
Populus nigra	

3. Cultivated Plants from the Formal Gardens, Hylands Park.

The following species were planted in the formal gardens and on the rose terrace 2000 – 2003 (apart from *).

Acanthus mollis	*Bellis* (Pink, Red, White)
Agapanthus	*Bergenia cordifolia* 'Purpurea'
Ageratum	*Canna* (Yellow)
Ajuga reptans 'Catlins Giant'	*Cortaderia selloana* var. *pumila**
Alchemilla mollis	*Crocosmia*
Anemone 'Whirlwind'	*Delphinium grandiflorum* 'Blue Butterfly'
Aquilegia vulgaris	*Dicentra spectabilis*
Arabis (Pink)	*Dryopteris erythrosora*
Aubrieta 'Purple Cascade'	*Echinacea purpurea* 'White Swan'

Echinops ritro 'Veitch's Blue'

Euphorbia characias 'Wulfenii'

Euphorbia dulcis 'Chameleon'

Geranium '*Magnificum*'

Geranium 'Maverick' (White/Orange)

Helleborus argutifolius

Helleborus orientalis

Heuchera regina

Hosta 'Francee'

Hosta sieboldiana

Iris 'Night Owl'

Iris 'Cliffs of Dover'

Liatris spicata '*Alba*'

Liatris spicata 'Floristan Violet'

Liriope muscari 'Ingwersen'

Lobelia 'Crystal Palace' (Blue/White)

Lysimachia punctata

Papaver orientalis (White/Pink)

Petunia 'Carpet' (Red/Blue)

Phyllitis scolopendrium

Scabiosa caucasica 'Perfecta Alba'

Scabiosa stafa

Stachys lanata

Tagetes 'Antigua' (Yellow/Orange)

Verbascum phoeniceum 'Pink Domino'

Veronica gentianoides 'Pallida'

Viola (Blue/White/Orange/Red/Yellow)

Roses

Charles Rennie Mackintosh

Charlotte

Glamis Castle

Heritage

Winchester Cathedral

Bulbs

Crocus*

Galanthus*

Narcissus*

Tulipa

Acer saccharinum

Geology and Soils

Dr Peter Allen and M.W.Hanson

Recorders : Dr Peter Allen, M.W.Hanson, Martin Heywood and G.R.Ward

Geology

In 2002 a shallow trench was excavated across Hylands Park, about a metre deep and several hundred metres in length, to accommodate a new high voltage electricity supply cable to the house. In November the trench (and spoil) was investigated for its geology.

The trench ran from approximately TL 688043 to TL 686044. The trench, nearest the formal gardens, exposed a pebbly clay. Downslope this was seen to overlie till (chalky boulder clay) and nearer to the eastern end of the trench, till was exposed immediately beneath the soil and was seen to overlie weathered London Clay. Pebbly clay was again exposed near the perimeter wall.

The stratigraphic sequence is interpreted as:

Pebbly clay	Head	Devensian	}	
			}	Quaternary
Chalky boulder clay	Great Waltham Till	Anglian	}	
Brown clay	London Clay	Eocene	Tertiary	

The till was considered to be typical of the Great Waltham variant of the Lowestoft Till. The exposure is rather further south than would be expected, but may have been deposited by a finger of ice that extended along what was to become the valley of the River Wid. This deposit is thought to date from the Anglian stage (about 450,000 years ago).

The pebbly clay was interpreted as head on the basis of its texture, position in the landscape and distribution. It contained a mixture of rounded, chatter-marked (Tertiary) and sub-angular flints of relatively local origin. There were also significant amounts of white/colourless vein quartz, occasionally with red staining, and brown and pink quartzites, originally from the Midlands. Rare pieces of grey-green igneous rock (rhyolite/tuff) from the Welsh borderlands and veined tourmaline (Lydian stone) probably originally from south-west England (eg Dartmoor) were also noted. This assemblage is typical of the Kesgrave (sand and gravel) Formation, deposited by an early Thames which crossed central Essex.

Local glacial outwash can have a similar assemblage, generally with more sub-angular flint but, importantly, also with *Rhaxella* chert, which is diagnostic of the glacial deposits. None of this chert was identified, but a sample has been collected for a laboratory stone count, to resolve this issue. The gravel, whatever its origin, subsequent to its deposition on higher ground over London Clay, soliflucted downslope, mixing with the clay to create the head. Some parts of the head extended beyond the general cover, moving down minor valley heads, cutting through the thin outcrop of till. The pebbly clay is thought to derive from the last glacial phase of the Pleistocene (25,000+ years ago).

The prevailing clay types of the underlying geology at Hylands explain why Hylands can be very muddy in wet winters and at other periods of heavy rainfall. It is not uncommon for vehicles driven off-road at these times to get set in the park. Heavy work, because of the potential (and actual) damage it can cause, should be scheduled for dry periods when the ground can support heavy vehicles, such as J.C.Bs and H.G.Vs. The prevalence of clay also probably indicates that drainage schemes are unlikely to be entirely successful and for conservation reasons should not be carried-out; impeded drainage is important for many species of plant.

The head deposits and chalky boulder clay almost certainly account, at least in part, for the mosaic of different grassland types found at Hylands, from the markedly acid in the formal gardens, to the calcareous till on Writtle Hills. This varying geology is a positive asset to the biodiversity of Hylands Park.

Alluvial deposits (recent) characterise the low-lying former flood meadows adjacent to the River Wid. Hylands has two fields – named Clay Pit Field and Brick Field – presumably the site of a former brick works, the London Clay providing the raw resource for the bricks. The previously-mentioned trench also provided evidence, in the form of small fragments of chalk (<5mm) in a layer in the soil profile, of marling in the past.

Soils

Analysis of three soil samples collected in 2002 from the formal gardens and Football Field gave the following results:

	Formal Gardens (1) TL 683044	Formal Gardens (2) TL 683043	Football Field (3) TL 679044
pH	4.9	6.0	5.7
Particle Size (%)			
Sand	32	37	22
Silt	43	40	54
Clay	25	23	24
Texture	Clay Loam	Clay Loam	Clay Loam
Extractable Elements (mg/l)			
Phosphorous	4	10	0.4
Potassium	85	276	97
Magnesium	53	22	125

The soil pH for all 3 samples is noticeably acid (neutral = 7) and particularly so for the sample collected in the vicinity of the acid grassland in the formal gardens (4.9). This area has *Calluna vulgaris, Galium saxatile, Carex ovalis* and two *Polytrichum* spp., as well as *Rhododendron*s. The calcareous grassland site on Writtle Hills (TL 680044) which supports *Primula veris, Briza media* and *Trifolium ochroleucon* should show a pH closer to alkaline – it was not possible, however, to sample this area. It presumably has a deposit of chalky boulder clay close to the surface.

Hylands – Habitats

Hylands is wood-pasture, although the grasslands are not managed through a formal grazing regime and the trees are not managed as pollards or as standards to provide timber. The grasslands are mown (some for amenity, some for hay) and the trees are managed for their visual and historic interest. Some grazing pressure is imposed by a herd of fallow deer, which access the whole park, but are not enclosed within the park.

The habitats present within the wood-pasture are varied and include:

Ancient Woodland (coppiced woodland and ancient trees in grassland)

Secondary Woodland (and mature and developing scrub)

Plantations and Belts

Formal Gardens

Old Kitchen Garden

Old Orchard (remains)

Green Lane (fragment)

Hedge Lines (Roman Walk)

Old Grassland (a mosaic-acid to calcareous)

Old Mown Grassland (formal garden lawns)

New Grassland (north part of Hylands, were cultivated fields until recently)

Ponds and Lakes (including "moat" and a watercress bed)

Brook (with riffle and pool)

River (River Wid, re-incorporated into the park)

Sedge 'Fen' (*Carex pendula* - developing)

Grasslands

Old Grassland
1. Back Park
2. Cut-throat Hall Field
3. Football Field (Home Pasture)
4. Front Park (N)
5. Front Park (S)
6. Great Wood Close
7. Great Wood Field
8. Ha Ha
9. Home Field
10. Lightfoot Garden
11. Long Broad Field
12. Sixteen Acres

Acid Grassland
13. Formal gardens (fragments)

Calcareous Grassland
14. Writtle Hills (Little Slipe) (fragments)

Box Mown
15. Formal gardens (inc. North Lawn)
Heavily mown
16. Lake Field
17. Clay Pit Field

New Grassland
18. New Park
19. Surry Mead
20. Ventrises Field
21. Walnut Tree Field
22. Widford Mead

Other
23. Brick Field
24. Hook Field
25. Green Car Park

Wooded Areas

Ancient woodland
1. Formal Gardens (fragment)
2. Lightfoot Spring
3. Lower Belt
4. South Wood
5. Tower Belt North
6. Writtle Wood

Secondary woodland
7. Lower Belt
8. South Wood Scrubs
9. South Wood Triangle

Plantations and Belts
10. Ash Plantation
11. Home farm Plantation
12. Ice-house Plantation
13. Lake Field Belt (part)
14. Lake Plantation

15. Lightfoot Plantation
16. London Road Belt
17. Lower Belt (part)
18. Margaretting Belt
19. Oak Plantation
20. Pigeon Plantation
21. Poplar Plantation
22. Rook Plantation
23. Swan Pond Plantation
24. Tower Belt (south)
25. Writtle Belt

Other
26. Formal Gardens
27. Green Lane
28. Margaretting hedge line
29. Old Orchard
30. Roman Walk

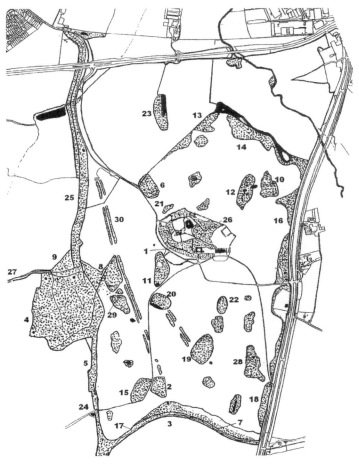

Freshwater Habitats

Ponds and Lakes
1. Ephemeral Pond
2. Formal Gardens Pond
3. Formal Gardens Lake
4. Home Farm Pond
5. Ice House Pond
6. Kitchen garden Pond
7. Lake Field Pond
8. Pigeon Pond
9. Plantation Pond
10. Serpentine Lake
11. South Wood Pond
12. South Wood Pond
13. South Wood Pond
14. Spring Pond
15. Swan Pond
16. Writtle Lodge Pond

Ponds and Lakes just outside park
17. Marconi Fishing Lake
18. Triangle Pond

'Sedge Fen' and wet areas
19. Ice house 'Sedge fen'
20. Lower Belt 'Sedge Fen'
21. Oak Plantation wet area

Others
22. Ha ha ditch
23. Moat
24. Site of Former Ponds
25. Water-cress Bed

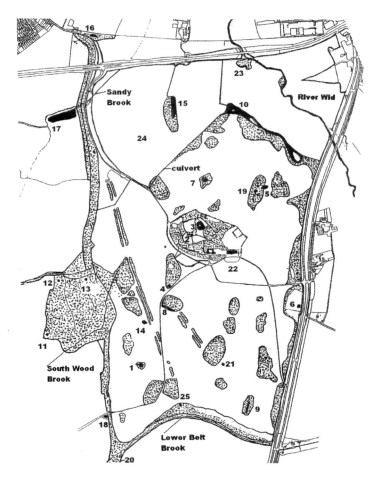

Diptera at Hylands Park

Del Smith & Mark Hanson

Introduction

The following chapter is based on Diptera recording undertaken at Hylands in the years 2001 – 2003. All the flies were collected by M.W.Hanson, for the most part using a net (a brief trial with a malaise trap was unsuccessful due to the public nature of the park) and a small amount of material was reared. The pinned material (apart from Syrphids) was subsequently determined by Del Smith. Particular attention was paid to the Diptera associated with the older trees in the park, in order to establish some idea of the conservation status of the site. Between 2001 and 2003, a total of 337 species of Diptera were recorded. In the appended list, species associated with the older trees (Saproxylics) are followed by the letter 'S'. The national conservation status (currently under review) of species is also added (either N = Notable or RDB = Red Data Book 1, 2 or 3). Despite 330 plus species being found, I suspect that the real total of Diptera species that could potentially be found in the park to be nearer the thousand mark, because of the diversity of habitat and also the rich variety of trees, shrubs and higher plants. A total of 17 nationally notable and four Red Data Book flies were recorded from the site. A minimum of 71 Saproxylic species were found.

Scarce and Unusual Species

The most notable species of fly from Hylands is the spectacular hoverfly *Callicera spinolae*. This species, along with the bumble-bee, mimic *Criorhina ranunculi* and the small Sepsid Fly *Themira gracilis* were all recorded as new to Essex. *Criorhina ranunculi* observed twice at rot-holes at the base of Horse Chestnut trees and once on the blossom of Cockspur Thorn (*Crataegus crus-galli*) is a very plausible bee mimic and with a very early flight season, is probably under-recorded in Essex. *Themira gracilis*, another nationally notable species with an apparently very disjunct distribution in Britain, being known mainly from the north of England and Scotland and then in the south in Hampshire and now in Essex, was swept from the edge of the Serpentine Lake in July 2002.

Callicera aurata (RDB 3) – another of the rare hoverflies, but more often recorded than the RDB 1 *C.spinolae* – was found at rest on an Ivy leaf in the formal gardens on September 12th 2002. Its larva, along with those of *C. spinolae*, have been recorded from rot-holes in various mature tree species. At Hylands it would almost certainly occur in Horse Chestnut. *Psilota anthracina* (RDB 2) is possibly the classic parkland hoverfly in Essex. It is known from Weald, Thorndon and Dagnam Parks, as well as Hylands. Elsewhere it also occurs in old forests, such as Windsor. *Didea fasciata* is a rarity in Essex, known only from a handful of sites. In Britain it is often recorded from ancient woodland, but is also found in secondary woodland and even gardens.

Dorycera graminum (RDB 3) is, as its specific name suggests, a grassland species. Although rarely recorded, in 2002–3 it has turned-up at several sites, mainly in south Essex and occasionally in large numbers. I noted a single specimen on grass near the Serpentine Lake in 2003.

Further Recording

Much more recording of Diptera needs to be undertaken, despite some 337 species from 61 families having so far been found. Even the hoverflies, the best studied group, have some notable gaps.

Despite what is arguably one of Britain's rarest invertebrates - *Callicera spinolae* - being found, some very common species – such as *Platycheirus scutatus* – are so far conspicuous by their absence from the list. The genus *Cheilosia* would also be a fruitful area for further recording and research. Some families are much under-recorded, especially among the nematocera, for example the crane-flies (Tipulidae) and non-biting midges (Chironomidae).

The freshwater habitats (including the ponds, lakes, brooks, river Wid and even the damp sedge fens) would repay further investigation. So far, none of the rarer aquatic soldier-flies (Stratiomyiidae) have been found. Passive sampling techniques – such as malaise, flight-interception and water traps – would no doubt enhance the number of species recorded.

Hoverflies (Syrphidae) at Hylands

Hoverflies as a family exploit a wide range of habitats. An extensive species list from a particular site is indicative of the habitats found there and can be used as an indication of the potential biodiversity of a particular site. Using the list for Hylands, it is clear that dry grassland (*Chrysotoxum verralli*), Marsh (*Lejogaster metallina*), Pond and ditch (*Parhelophilus frutetorum*) and gardens (*Merodon equestris, Eumerus funeralis* and *Volucella inanis*) are present. However, the most notable group - and most strongly represented - are the saproxylic hoverflies typical of lowland wood-pasture, some of which are not only rare in the U.K., but are scarce at a European level.

Hylands is unique in Essex; at no other site has the following assemblage of rare and scarce hoverflies been recorded. The list includes species which have yet to be found at some of the most important wood-pasture sites in Essex (including Epping Forest, Hatfield Forest, Thorndon Park, Weald Park and Dagnam Park). The list also gives an indication of the national and county conservation status of a species. However, the national status of scarce and threatened flies in the U.K. is currently under review.

The latest biodiversity list for East Anglia (published May 1998) gives a list of species of conservation concern for East Anglia (Cambs, Essex, Lincs, Norfolk and Suffolk). Two of the six hoverflies on the list – *Callicera spinolae* and *Psilota anthracina* – are known from Hylands.

In addition, *Callicera spinolae* is included in the Biodiversity U.K. Steering Group Report. It is a species considered to be declining throughout its range in Europe.

Diptera : Syrphidae

Britain	-	271 named species
Essex	-	183 named species (total)
Essex	-	172 named species (last 50 years)
Hylands	-	79 named species (2001 – 2003)

Some Hoverflies Recorded From Hylands 2001 – 2003

Essex statuses and their definitions are given in the provisional Essex Red Data list at
www.essexfieldclub.org.uk/ERDlist/ERDB.htm

	National Status	Essex Rarity Status	Essex Threat Status
Brachyopa insensilis	N	Scarce	Threatened
Brachyopa scutellaris	-	-	-
Brachypalpoides lentus	-	-	-
Callicera aurata	RDB 3	Rare	Threatened
Callicera spinolae	RDB 1	Rare	Endangered
Chalcosyrphus nemorum	-	-	-
Criorhina asilica	N	Rare	Threatened
Criorhina berberina	-	-	-
Criorhina floccosa	-	-	-
Criorhina ranunculi	N	Rare	Endangered
Didea fasciata	N	Rare	Threatened
Epistrophe diaphana	N	Rare	Threatened
Meligramma triangulifera	N	Scarce	-
Myolepta dubia	N	Scarce	-
Psilota anthracina	RDB 2	Rare	Vulnerable
Scaeva selenitica	-	-	-
Volucella inanis	N	Scarce	Regionally Important
Xylota xanthocnema	N	Scarce	-

Also of note, at no other site in Essex have all four British members of the genus *Criorhina* – both
southern species of *Callicera* and *Psilota anthracina* – been found.

Diptera on Ivy at Hylands

Ivy is a particularly useful nectar source, attracting many insects late in the year. Hylands currently has Ivy in some quantity – particularly on the perimeter wall of the kitchen garden and in the formal gardens. The following flies were recorded on Ivy during September – November 2001 and 2002 from the formal gardens. Hornets were a notable predatory species on the Ivy – seen taking *Eristalis tenax* and other flies.

Baccha elongata	*Myatropa florea*
Callicera aurata (on leaf)	*Phaonia errans*
Callicera spinolae	*Phaonia mediterranea*
Cheilosia scutellata	*Phaonia populi*
Didea fasciata	*Phasia hemiptera*
Episyrphus balteatus	*Platycheirus albimanus*
Epistrophe grossulariae	*Pollenia angustigena*
Eristalis pertinax	*Pollenia pediculata*
Eristalis tenax	*Riponnensia splendens*
Eudasyphora cyanella	*Siphona geniculata*
Melanostoma mellinum	*Syrphus ribesii*
Melanostoma scalare	*Thaumatomyia notata*
Meliscaeva cinctella	*Volucella pellucens*
Mesembrina meridiana	*Musca autumnalis*

References

Chandler, P.J. (ed.) (1998) Diptera. Checklists of Insects in the British Isles Vol. 12 pt. 1. Royal Entomological Society

Damant, S. (2002) Further Hoverflies at Wimpole Hall, Bulletin of the Dipterists Forum No. 53 Spring 2002

Falk, S. (1991) A review of the scarce and threatened flies of Great Britain (Part 1) (Nature Conservancy Council)

Harvey, P. (2002) Essex Red Data List – Consultation draft (Privately Published) Uttp:// www.essexfieldclub.org.uk./.

Pont, A. (1979) Sepsidae Hndbk.Ident.Brit.Ins. Vol X part 5 (c) Royal Entomological Society

Simonson, W. & Thomas, R. (1999) Biodiversity – Making The Links. English Nature

Speight, M.C.D. (1989) Saproxylic Invertebrates and their Conservation. Nature and Environment Series No. 42 Council of Europe. Strasbourg

Stubbs, A. and Falk, S. (2002) British Hoverflies. An Illustrated Identification Guide. British Entomological and Natural History Society

Stubbs, A. and Chandler, P. (1978) A Dipterists Handbook. The Amateur Entomologist Vol. 15. The Amateur Entomologists Society

SPECIES LIST   **S = Saproxylic**

The checklist followed is Chandler (1998) Checklists of insects of the British Isles (New Series) Part 1: Diptera. *Handbooks for the identification of British insects*. Royal Entomological Society.

TIPULIDAE
Dictenidia bimaculata Linnaeus   S
Nephrotoma flavipalpis (Meigen)
Nephrotoma quadrifaria (Meigen)
Tipula fascipennis Meigen
Tipula flavolineata Meigen   S
Tipula vernalis Meigen
  LIMONIDAE
Dicranomyia modesta (Meigen)
Epiphragma ocellare (Linnaeus)
Euphylidorea lineola (Meigen)
Gnophomyia viridipennis (Gimmerthal)
Limonia maculipennis (Meigen)
Limonia nubeculosa Meigen
Limonia phragmitidis (Schrank)
  BIBIONIDAE
Bibio johannis (Linnaeus)
Bibio marci (Linnaeus)
Dilophus febrilis (Linnaeus)
  DITOMYIIDAE
Symmerus annulatus (Meigen)   S
  KEROPLATIDAE
Cerotelion striatum (Gmelin)   S
Isoneuromyia semirufa (Meigen)   S
Macrocera crassicornis Winnertz   S   N
Macrocera fasciata Meigen   S
Macrocera stigma Curtis   S
Neoplatyura modesta (Winnertz)   S
Orfelia fasciata (Meigen)   S
Orfelia nemoralis (Meigen)   S
  MYCETOPHILIDAE
Leia crucigera Zetterstedti
Mycomya wankowiczii Dziedzicki   S
  CECIDOMYIIDAE
Contarinia tiliarum (Kieffer)
Cystiphora sonchi (Bremi)
Dasineura crataegi (Winnertz)
Dasineura urticae (Perris)
Didimomyia tiliacea (Bremi)
Hartigiola annulipes (Hartig)
Rhopalomyia millefolii (Loew)
Rondaniola bursaria (Bremi)
Taxomyia taxi (Inchbold)
  PSYCHODIDAE
Trichomyia urbica Haliday   S
  MYCETOBIIDAE
Mycetobia pallipes Meigen   S   N

SCATOPSIDAE
Apiloscatopse flavicollis (Meigen)
Ectaetia platyscelis (Loew)   S
CULICIDAE
Culiseta annulata (Schrank)
CHIRONIMIDAE
Ablabesmyia monilis (Linnaeus)
RHAGIONIDAE
Chrysopilus asiliformis (Preyssler)
Rhagio lineola Fabricius
Rhagio scolopaceus (Linnaeus)
Rhagio tringarius (Linnaeus)
TABANIDAE
Haematopota pluvialis (Linnaeus)
Tabanus autumnalis Linnaeus
XYLOMYIIDAE
Solva marginata (Meigen)   S   N
STRATIOMYIIDAE
Beris chalybeata (Forster)
Chloromyia formosa (Scopoli)
Chorisops nagatomii Rozkosny
Pachygaster atra (Panzer)   S
Praomyia leachii Stephens   S
Sargus bipunctatus (Scopoli)
BOMBYLIIDAE
Bombylius major Linnaeus
THEREVIDAE
Thereva nobilitata (Fabricius)
ASILIDAE
Choerades marginatus (Linnaeus)   S   N
Dioctria linearis (Fabricius)
Leptogaster cylindrica (De Geer)
HYBOTIDAE
Bicellaria vana Collin
Hybos culiciformis (Fabricius)
Leptopeza flavipes (Meigen)   S
Oedalia flavipes Zetterstedt   S
Platypalpus longiseta (Zetterstedt)
Platypalpus luteus (Meigen)
Platypalpus notatus (Meigen)
Platypalpus pallipes (Fallen)
Platypalpus pectoralis (Fallen)
Tachydromia aemula (Loew)
Tachypeza nubila (Meigen)   S
EMPIDIDAE
Chelifera precatoria (Fallen)
Clinocera stagnalis (Haliday)
Empis albinervis Meigen
Empis caudatula Loew

Empis livida Linnaeus
Empis lutea Meigen
Empis nuntia Meigen
Empis tesselata Fabricius
Empis trigramma Wiedemann
Hilara anglodanica Lundbeck
Hilara brevistyla Collin
Hilara lurida Fallen
Hilara thoracica Macquart
MICROPHORIDAE
Microphorus holosericeus (Meigen)
DOLICHOPODIDAE
Argyra leucocephala (Meigen)
Chrysotimus flaviventris von Roser
Chrysotus blepharosceles Kowartz
Chrysotus gramineus (Fallen)
Dolichopus griseipennis Stannius
dolichopus wahlbergi Zetterstedt
Hercostomus parvilamellatus (Macquart)
Medetera jacula (Fallen)   S
Medetera truncorum Meigen   S
Neurigona quadrifasciata (Fabricius)
Poecilobothrus nobilitatus (Linnaeus)
Rhaphium appendiculatum Zetterstedt
Rhaphium caliginosum Meigen
Scellus notatus (Fabricius)
Sciapus platypterus (Fabricius)   S
Sybistroma obscurellum (Fallen)
Sympycnus desoutteri Parent
Syntormon denticulatus (Zetterstedt)
Syntormon pallipes (Fabricius)
Systenus scholtzii (Loew)   S   N
Systenus pallipes (von Roser)   S   N
PLATYPEZIDAE
Bolopus furcatus Fallen   S
Platypeza consobrina Zetterstedt   S
Platypeza fasciata Meigen   S
Protoclythia modesta (Zetterstedt)   S
Protoclythia rufa (Meigen)   S
PHORIDAE
Borophaga carinifrons (Zetterstedt)
LONCHOPTERIDAE
Lonchoptera bifurcata (Fallen)
Lonchoptera lutea Panzer
SYRPHIDAE
Baccha elongata (Fabricius)
Brachyopa insensilis Collin   S   N
Brachyopa scutellaris Robineau-Desvoidy   S
Brachypalpoides lentus (Meigen)   S
Callicera aurata (Rossi)   S   RDB3

Callicera spinolae Rondani	S	RDB1
Chalcosyrphus nemorum (Fabricius)	S	
Cheilosia albitarsis (Meigen)		
Cheilosia bergenstammi Becker		
Cheilosia illustrata (Harris)		
Cheilosia impressa Loew		
Cheilosia pagana (Meigen)		
Cheilosia scutellata (Fallen)		
Cheilosia variabilis (Panzer)		
Chrysogaster solstitialis (Fallen)		
Chrysotoxum bicinctum (Linnaeus)		
Chrysotoxum verralli Collin		
Criorhina asilica (Fallen)	S	N
Criorhina berberina (Fabricius)	S	
Criorhina floccosa (Meigen)	S	
Criorhina ranunculi (Panzer)	S	N
Dasysyrphus albostriatus (Fallen)		
Dasysyrphus tricinctus (Fallen)		
Didea fasciata Macquart		N
Epistrophe diaphana (Zetterstedt)		N
Epistrophe elegans (Harris)		
Epistrophe grossulariae (Meigen)		
Episyrphus balteatus (De Geer)		
Eristalinus sepulchralis (Linnaeus)		
Eristalis arbustorum (Linnaeus)		
Eristalis interruptus (Poda)		
Eristalis intricarius (Linnaeus)		
Eristalis pertinax (Scopoli)		
Eristalis tenax (Linnaeus)		
Eumerus funeralis (Meigen)		
Eumerus strigatus (Fallen)		
Eupeodes corollae (Fabricius)		
Eupeodes latifasciatus (Macquart)		
Eupeodes luniger (Meigen)		
Ferdinandea cuprea (Scopoli)	S	
Helophilus pendulus (Linnaeus)		
Heringia heringi (Zetterstedt)		
Lejogaster metallina (Fabricius)		
Leucozona lucorum (Linnaeus)		
Melangyna cincta Fallen		
Melangyna compos/labiat		
Melanogaster hirtella (Loew)		
Melanostoma mellinum (Linnaeus)		
Melanostoma scalare (Fabricius)		
Meligramma triangulifera (Zetterstedt)		N
Meliscaeva auricollis (Meigen)		
Merodon equestris (Fabricius)		
Myathropa florea (Linnaeus)		
Myolepta dubia (Fabricius)	S	N
Neoascia podagrica (Fabricius)		

Parhelophilus frutetorum (Fabricius)
Pipiza austriaca Meigen
Pipiza fenestrata Meigen
Pipiza luteitarsis Zetterstedt
Platycheirus albimanus (Fabricius)
Platycheirus clypeatus (Meigen)
Platycheirus manicatus (Meigen)
Platycheirus rosarum (Fabricius)
Platycheirus tarsalis (Schummel)
Psilota anthracina Meigen   S   RDB2
Rhingia campestris Meigen
Ripponensia splendens (Meigen)
Scaeva pyrastri (Linnaeus)
Scaeva selenitica (Meigen)
Syritta pipiens (Linnaeus)
Syrphus ribesii (Linnaeus)
Syrphus torvus Osten Sacken
Syrphus vitripennis Meigen
Volucella bombylans (Linnaeus)
Volucella inanis (Linnaeus)   N
Volucella pellucens (Linnaeus)
Xylota segnis (Linnaeus)
Xylota sylvarum (Linnaeus)   S
Xylota xanthocnema Collin   S   N
MICROPEZIDAE
Neria cibaria (Linnaeus)
MEGAMERINIDAE
Megamerina dolium (Fabricius)   S   N
PSILIDAE
Chamaepsila obscuritarsis (Loew)
CONOPIDAE
Sicus ferrugineus (Linnaeus)
LONCHAEIDAE
Lonchaea contigua Collin   S
Lonchaea limatula Collin   S
PALLOPTERIDAE
Palloptera muliebris (Harris)   S
Palloptera umbellatarum (Fabricius)   S
Palloptera ustulata Fallen   S
PIOPHILIDAE
Parapiophila vulgaris (Fallen)
Stearibia nigriceps (Meigen)
ULIDIIDAE
Dorycera graminum (Fabricius)   RDB3
Herina longistylata Rivosecchi
Otites guttata (Meigen)
PLATYSTOMATIDAE
Platystoma seminationis (Fabricius)
TEPHRITIDAE
Acanthiophilus helianthi (Rossi)   N

Chaetorellia jaceae (Robineau-Desvoidy)
Orellia falcata (Scopoli)
Philophylla caesio (Harris)
Tephritis formosa (Loew)
Terellia ruficauda (Fabricius)
Terellia tussilaginis (Fabricius)
Urophora cardui (Linnaeus)
Urophora stylata (Fabricius)
Xyphosia miliaria (Schrank)
LAUXANIIDAE
Calliopum aeneum (Fallen)
Calliopum simillimum Collin
Meiosimyza decipiens (Loew)
Meiosimyza platycephala (Loew)
Meiosimyza rorida (Fallen)
Minettia inusta (Meigen)
Minettia longipennis (Fabricius)
Peplomyza litura (Meigen)
Pseudolyciella stylata Papp
Sapromyza halidayi Shatalkin
Sapromyza quadricincta Becker
Tricholauxania praeusta (Fallen)
DRYOMYZIDAE
Neuroctena anilis (Fallen)
PHAEOMYIIDAE
Pelidnoptera fuscipennis (Meigen)
SCIOMYZIDAE
Hydromya dorsalis (Fabricius)
Ilione albiseta (Scopoli)
Limnia unguicornis (Scopoli)
Pherbellia dubia (Fallen)
Tetanocera hyalipennis von Roser
Trypetoptera punctulata (Scopoli)
SEPSIDAE
Sepsis cynipsea (Linnaeus)
Themira gracilis (Zetterstedt)   N
CLUSIIDAE
Clusia flava (Meigen)   S
Clusiodes albimanus (Meigen)   S
Clusiodes gentilis (Collin)   S
ODINIIDAE
Odinia boletina (Zetterstedt)   S
AGROMYZIDAE
Chromatomyia nigra (Meigen)
OPOMYZIDAE
Opomyza florum (Fabricius)
Opomyza germinationis (Linnaeus)
Opomyza petrei Mesnil
AULACIGASTERIDAE
Aulacigaster leucopeza (Meigen)   S

ASTEIIDAE
Asteia amoena Meigen   S
Leiomyza dudai Sabrosky   S
CHLOROPIDAE
Elachiptera cornuta (Fallen)
Elachiptera tuberculifera (Corti)
Lasiambia brevibucca (Duda)   S
Oscinella caticiphila Collin
Thaumatomyia notata (Meigen)
HELEOMYZIDAE
Heteromyza rotundicornis (Zetterstedt)
Neoleria ruficeps (Zetterstedt)   S
Suillia affinis (Meigen)   S
Suillia atricornis (Meigen)   S
Suillia notata (Meigen)   S
Suillia pallida (Fallen)   S
Suillia variegata (Loew)
Tephrochlamys flavipes (Zetterstedt)
Tephrochlamys rufiventris (Meigen)
SPHAEROCERIDAE
Copromyza nigrina (Gimmerthal)
Crumomyia fimetaria (Meigen)
Crumomyia roserii (Rondani)
Ischiolepta pusilla (Fallen)
Leptocera fontinalis (Fallen)
Opacifrons coxata (Stenhammar)
Pteremis fenestralis (Fallen)
Pullimosina moesta (Villeneuve)
Spelobia parapusio (Dahl)
Sphaerocera curvipes Latrielle
DROSOPHILIDAE
Cacoxenus indagator Loew
Drosophila confusa Staeger   S
Drosophila immigrans Sturtevant
Drosophila obscura Fallen
Drosophila subobscura Collin
Leucophenga maculata (Dufour)   S
Scaptomyza graminum (Fallen)
Scaptomyza pallida (Zetterstedt)
CAMPICHOETIDAE
Campichoeta punctum (Meigen)
EPHYDRIDAE
Ditichophora calceata (Meigen)
Notiphila maculata Stenhammar
SCATHOPHAGIDAE
Cordilura albipes Fallen
Nanna armillata (Zetterstedt)
Nanna fasciata (Meigen)
Norellia spinipes (Meigen)
Norellisoma spinimanum (Fallen)

Scathophaga furcata (Say)
Scathophaga inquinata Meigen
Scathophaga stercoraria (Linnaeus)
ANTHOMYIIDAE
Eustalomyia histrio (Zetterstedt)
FANNIIDAE
Fannia canicularis (Linnaeus)
Fannia corvina (Verrall)
Fannia monilis (Haliday)
Fannia pallitibia (Rondani)
Fannia polychaeta (Stein)
Fannia similis (Stein)
MUSCIDAE
Azelia nebulosa Robineau-Desvoidy
Coenosia agromyzina (Fallen)
Coenosia albicornis Meigen
Coenosia mollicula (Fallen)
Coenosia tigrina (Fabricius)
Eudasyphora cyanella (Meigen)
Helina pertusa (Meigen)
Hydrotaea cyrtoneurina (Zetterstedt)
Hydrotaea ignava (Harris)
Mesembrina meridiana (Linnaeus)
Musca autumnalis De Geer
Musca domestica Linnaeus
Phaonia cincta (Zetterstedt)   S
Phaonia errans (Meigen)
Phaonia halterata (Stein)
Phaonia mediterranea Hennig
Phaonia pallida (Fabricius)   S
Phaonia palpata (Stein)   S
Phaonia rufiventris (Scopoli)
Phaonia subventa (Harris)
Phaonia tuguriorum (Scopoli)
Phaonia valida Harris
Potamia littoralis Robineau-Desvoidy
Thricops diaphanus (Wiedemann)
CALLIPHORIDAE
Calliphora vicina Robineau-Desvoidy
Lucilia caesar (Linnaeus)
Pollenia angustigena Wainwright
Pollenia pediculata Macquart
Pollenia rudis (Fabricius)
Protocalliphora azurea (Fallen)
TACHINIDAE
Eriothrix rufomaculata (De Geer)
Gymnochaeta viridis (Fallen)
Phasia hemiptera (Fabricius)
Siphona geniculata (De Geer)
Tachina fera (Linnaeus)

Coleoptera at Hylands Park

Peter Hammond & Mark Hanson

Introduction

No recording of beetles in this interesting example of a pseudo-Medieval park appears to have been done until the 1960s when a little general collecting of these insects was done by Peter Hammond. The data from these collections and from later investigations, by Peter Hammond and by Mark Hanson in the 2000-2003 period, have been assembled to produce the account of Hylands Park Coleoptera presented here. Some 416 beetle species are now listed for the Park. In view of the varied terrain of Hylands Park, incorporating woodland, herb-rich grassland, open parkland with overmature native trees, gardens and a range of ponds, and now including a stretch of the River Wid, this total may represent approaching one half of the number of beetle species actually present at the site. Twenty of the species listed below are categorised as Nationally Notable (N, Na or Nb) by Hyman & Parsons (1992, 1994). Information on the previous occurrence in Essex of these species is provided by Hammond (1999, 2000).

Scarce and unusual species

For four of the species found at Hylands Park there are no previous Essex records. Two of these – *Gyrophaena bihamata* and *Orthoperus nigrescens* – are relatively widespread (but generally woodland associated) species that may be expected to occur more widely in Essex. *Cossonus linearis* is a little recorded species that is known from scattered sites in south-east England (Morris, 2002). Most usually associated with moist decaying wood of poplars and willows, the host tree (an ancient ash) in which a single individual of the species was found in May 2001 in Hylands Park is unusual. *Atomaria turgida* has only recently been recognised as British on the basis of specimens collected in Monmouthshire in 1996 (Levey & Pavett, 1999b); it may be a recent immigrant to the British Isles; I have also seen a recently collected specimen from the Banchory district, Scotland. A single individual of this species was taken from flood debris beside the River Wid at the northern end of Hylands Park by Peter Hammond in February 2003.

Several of the 'saproxylic' species (see below) were previously known in Essex only from the general area of Epping Forest (including Hainault Forest) and/or Hatfield Forest. These include *Nemadus colonoides*, *Xantholinus angularis*, *Euplectus infirmus*, *Prionocyphon serricornis* and *Ptinus sexpunctatus*. The last-mentioned, like a number of other 'spider beetles', may be found in and around buildings, but the species is also typically found in the dry parts of ancient, especially hollow, deciduous trees. At Hylands Park a number of *P. sexpunctatus* were found in the hay loft of the stable block

Saproxylic species

A principal interest of Hylands Park from the perspective of its resident Coleoptera is the range of mature and over-mature native trees, especially the English Oak (*Quercus robur*). These are scattered through the park, with the greatest concentration of large oaks to be found in the open areas west of the house. Some 79 of the beetle species so far recorded from Hylands Park may be regarded as 'saproxylics', i.e. species associated in one way or another with dead or dying wood (see Hammond

& Harding (1991) Fowles *et al.* (1999) & Alexander (2002) for fuller definitions and discussion). A number of these are not especially fastidious species, and may be found where suitable habitat in the way of dead wood or arboricolous fungi occur in most parts of Essex. Some, however, are of much more restricted occurrence. In addition to those already mentioned above that otherwise are not known to occur in Essex beyond the Epping and Hatfield Forest areas, a further ten saproxylic species are, on the evidence available, very locally distributed in the county. These are *Hapalaraea pygmaea, Agrilus laticornis, Tillus elongatus, Pseudocistela ceramboides, Prionychus ater, Orchesia undulata, Mordellistena abdominalis, Ischnomera cyanea, Acalles misellus* and *Scolytus intricatus*.

Using the approach proposed by Fowles *et al.* (1999), the potential significance of Hylands Park for saproxylic beetle species may be evaluated. The 74 saproxylic species recorded here from Hylands Park (see Species List below), which are listed and given "rarity scores" by Fowles *et al.* (1999), produce a Saproxylic Quality Score for the site of 220. The Saproxylic Quality Index obtained is 291.2, very substantially lower than that (598.0) given for Epping Forest by Fowles *et al.* (1999), and also much lower than the Indexes that would be calculated for Hatfield Forest (A.B. Drane, 2001) and for Hainault Forest (P. Kirby, unpublished). Indeed, 49 of the 56 UK woodland sites for which Fowles *et al.* provide provisional SQIs, have indexes higher than 291.2. Nevertheless, in an Essex context, it may reasonably be expected that rather few woodland, wood-pasture or parkland sites beyond the limits of the Epping and Hatfield forest areas harbour a greater number of the more localised saproxylic beetle species.

References

Alexander, K.N.A. 2002. The invertebrates of living and decaying timber in Britain & Ireland. *English Nature Research Reports* **467**: 1-142.

Drane, A. B. 2001. *Saproxylic Coleoptera Survey of Hatfield Forest, Essex.* Unpublished report to the National Trust.

Fowles, A.P., Alexander, K.N.A. & Key, R.S. 1999. The Saproxylic Quality Index: evaluating wooded habitats for the conservation of dead-wood Coleoptera. *Coleopterist* **8**(3): 121-141.

Hammond, P.M. 1995. *Coleoptera in Epping Forest.* Unpublished report to English Nature and The Corporation of London. London: The Natural History Museum.

Hammond, P.M. 1999. The status in Essex of nationally scarce and threatened species of Coleoptera. *Essex Naturalist (New Series)* **17**: 173-190.

Hammond, P.M. 2000. The millennial status in Essex of nationally scarce and threatened species of Coleoptera. *Essex Naturalist (New Series)* **16**: 145-154.

Hammond, P.M. & Harding, P.T. 1991. Saproxylic invertebrate assemblages in British woodlands and their evaluation. *In:* H.J. Read (ed.) *Pollard and veteran tree management*, pp.29-37. Slough: Richmond Publishing.

Hyman, P.S. (revised Parsons, M.S.) 1992. *A review of the scarce and threatened Coleoptera of Great Britain.* Part 1. UK Nature Conservation: 3. Peterborough: Joint Nature Conservation Committee.

Hyman, P.S. (revised Parsons, M.S.) 1994. *A review of the scarce and threatened Coleoptera of Great Britain.* Part 2. UK Nature Conservation: 12. Peterborough: Joint Nature Conservation Committee.

Levey, B. & Pavett, P.M. 1999. Annual Exhibition, Imperial College, London SW7, 31st October 1998. *British Journal of Entomology and Natural History* **12**: 175.

Morris, M.G. 2002. True weevils (Part I), Coleoptera: Curculionidae (Subfamilies Raymondionyminae to Smicronychinae). *Handbooks for the Identification of British Insects* **5**(17b): 1-149.

Species list

1 = found by P.M. Hammond in 1967 (dates of visits: 31 March, 2 May, 1 June, 22 July, 29 July, 31 July)
2 = found by P.M. Hammond during visit on 12 May 2001
3 = found by P.M. Hammond during visit on 21 February 2003
4 = found by P.M. Hammond during visit on 13 May 2003
5 = found by M. Hanson, 2001-2003 (various dates)
S = saproxylic species; those listed by Fowles, Alexander & Key (1999) are indicated in bold type.

CARABIDAE

Leistus spinibarbis (Fabricius)	5
Nebria brevicollis (Fabricius)	1,5
Notiophilus biguttatus (Fabricius)	3,4,5
Notiophilus palustris (Duftschmid)	3
Notiophilus rufipes Curtis	1
Bembidion biguttatum (Fabricius)	3
Bembidion guttula (Fabricius)	1,3,4
Bembidion harpaloides Serville	3
Bembidion lampros (Herbst)	3,4
Bembidion lunulatum (Fourcroy)	1,3
Bembidion obtusum Serville	1,3,4
Bembidion 4-maculatum (Linnaeus)	3,4,5
Bembidion tetracolum Say	3,4
Stomis pumicatus (Panzer)	4,5
Pterostichus cupreus (Linnaeus)	5
Pterostichus madidus (Fabricius)	1
Pterostichus melanarius (Illiger)	1
Pterostichus minor (Gyllenhal)	1
Pterostichus strenuus (Panzer)	1,3,4
Pterostichus vernalis (Panzer)	1,3,4
Abax parallelepipedus (Piller & Mitterpacher)	1,2
Calathus melanocephalus (Linnaeus)	1
Calathus piceus (Marsham)	1
Agonum albipes (Fabricius)	5
Agonum dorsale (Pontoppidan)	2,3
Agonum obscurum (Herbst)	1
Amara lunicollis Schiödte	1
Amara plebeja (Gyllenhal)	3
Amara similata (Gyllenhal)	5
Harpalus affinis (Schrank)	5
Bradycellus harpalinus (Serville)	1
Badister bipustulatus (Fabricius)	3
Demetrias atricapillus (Linnaeus)	1,3
Dromius linearis (Olivier)	3,5
Dromius melanocephalus Dejean	3,4
Dromius 4-notatus (Zenker *in* Panzer)	1
Metabletus obscuroguttatus (Duftschmid)	3

HALIPLIDAE
Haliplus ruficollis (Degeer)   1
DYTISCIDAE
Hyphydrus ovatus (Linnaeus)   5
Hygrotus inaequalis (Fabricius)   5
Suphrodytes dorsalis (Fabricius)   5
Hydroporus palustris (Linnaeus)   5
Hydroporus planus (Fabricius)   5
Agabus bipustulatus (Linnaeus)   5
Dytiscus sp.   5
HYDROPHILIDAE
Helophorus aequalis Thomson   5
Helophorus grandis Illiger   5
Helophorus brevipalpis Bedel   1
Helophorus obscurus Mulsant   5
Cercyon convexiusculus Stephens   1   **Nb**
Cercyon haemorrhoidalis (Fabricius)   5
Cercyon impressus (Sturm)   1
Cercyon lateralis (Marsham)   1
Cercyon melanocephalus (Linnaeus)   1
Cercyon sternalis Sharp   1,3   **Nb**
Megasternum obscurum (Marsham)   1,3,5
Cryptopleurum minutum (Fabricius)   1
Hydrobius fuscipes (Linnaeus)   1
HISTERIDAE
Abraeus globosus (J. Hoffmann)   1,3,5 S
Dendrophilus punctatus (Herbst)   4
Paromalus flavicornis (Herbst)   5   S
Onthophilus striatus (Forster)   1
Paralister carbonarius (J. Hoffmann)   1
HYDRAENIDAE
Octhebius minimus (Fabricius)   3
PTILIIDAE
Nossidium pilosellum (Marsham)   5   S   N
Ptenidium fuscicorne Erichson   3
Ptenidium intermedium Wankowicz   4
Ptenidium laevigatum Erichson   1   S
Ptenidium nitidum (Heer)   1
Ptenidium pusillum (Gyllenhal)   1
Ptinella aptera (Guérin-Méneville)   1,5   S
Pteryx suturalis (Heer)   1   S
Acrotrichis atomaria (Degeer)   1
Acrotrichis intermedia (Gillmeister)   1
Acrotrichis sitkaensis (Motschulsky)   1
LEIODIDAE
Anisotoma humeralis (Fabricius)   1   S
Anisotoma orbicularis (Herbst)   1   S
Agathidium varians Beck   1   S
Ptomaphagus medius Rey   1

Ptomaphagus subvillosus (Goeze)	1	
Nemadus colonoides (Kraatz)	5	S
Nargus velox (Spence)	4	
Choleva angustata (Fabricius)	5	
SILPHIDAE		
Nicrophorus vespillo (Linnaeus)	5	
Necrodes littoralis (Linnaeus)	5	
SCYDMAENIDAE		
Eutheia scydmaenoides Stephens	1	N
Stenichnus scutellaris (P.W.J. Müller & Kunze)	3,5	
STAPHYLINIDAE		
Scaphisoma agaricinum (Linnaeus)	1	S
Metopsia retusa (Stephens)	1	
Megarthrus denticollis (Beck)	1	
Proteinus macropterus (Gravenhorst)	1	
Proteinus ovalis Stephens	1	
Anthobium atrocephalum (Gyllenhal)	1	
Anthobium unicolor (Marsham)	3	
Olophrum piceum (Gyllenhal)	1,3	
Lesteva heeri Fauvel	3,4	
Phyllodrepa floralis (Paykull)	1	S
Dropephylla ioptera (Stephens)	1	S
Hapalaraea pygmaea (Paykull)	5	S
Phloeonomus punctipennis Thomson	1	S
Syntomium aeneum (P.W.J. Müller)	1	
Carpelimus bilineatus Stephens	3	
Carpelimus corticinus (Gravenhorst)	3	
Carpelimus elongatulus (Erichson)	3,4,5	
Platystethus nitens (C.R. Sahlberg)	3	
Anotylus mutator (Lohse)	5	N
Anotylus rugosus (Fabricius)	1,3,4,5	
Anotylus sculpturatus (Gravenhorst)	3	
Anotylus tetracarinatus (Block)	1	
Oxytelus laqueatus (Marsham)	1	
Oxyporus rufus (Linnaeus)	5	
Stenus aceris Stephens	3,4	
Stenus bimaculatus Gyllenhal	3,5	
Stenus binotatus Ljungh	1	
Stenus boops Ljungh	4	
Stenus brunnipes Stephens	3	
Stenus butrintensis Smetana	1	N
Stenus canaliculatus Gyllenhal	3	
Stenus clavicornis (Scopoli)	1,3	
Stenus flavipes Stephens	1	
Stenus fulvicornis Stephens	1,3	
Stenus impressus Germar	1	
Stenus juno (Paykull)	1	
Stenus ossium Stephens	3,4	
Stenus pallitarsis Stephens	1	

Stenus pusillus Stephens	3,4		
Stenus similis (Herbst)	5		
Lathrobium brunnipes (Fabricius)	1,3,4		
Lathrobium geminum Kratz	1,5		
Sunius propinquus (Brisout)	1,3,4		
Othius angustus Stephens	1		
Othius punctulatus (Goeze)	3		
Atrecus affinis (Paykull)	1,2,5	S	
Gyrohypnus fracticornis (O.F. Müller)	1		
Xantholinus angularis Ganglbauer	5	S	**Na**
Xantholinus linearis (Olivier)	1,3		
Xantholinus longiventris Heer	3,5		
Philonthus fimetarius (Gravenhorst)	1		
Philonthus marginatus (Ström)	1		
Philonthus politus (Linnaeus)	5		
Philonthus sordidus (Gravenhorst)	1		
Philonthus tenuicornis Mulsant & Rey	1		
Philonthus varius (Gyllenhal)	3,5		
Philonthus splendens (Fabricius)	1		
Philonthus subuliformis (Gravenhorst)	5	S	
Philonthus succicola Thomson	1		
Philonthus umbratilis (Gravenhorst)	5		
Gabrius appendiculatus Sharp	3		
Gabrius breviventer (Rey)	3		
Gabrius nigritulus (Gravenhorst)	3		
Gabrius piliger Mulsant & Rey	1		
Gabrius splendidulus (Gravenhorst)	2	S	
Ocypus olens (O. Müller)	1		
Tasgius melanarius (Heer)	1,5		
Creophilus maxillosus (Linnaeus)	5		
Heterothops minutus Wollaston	1		
Quedius cruentus (Olivier)	1		
Quedius curtipennis Bernhauer	3		
Quedius fuliginosus (Gravenhorst)	3		
Quedius humeralis Stephens	5		
Quedius mesomelinus (Marsham)	1		
Quedius picipes (Mannerheim)	4		
Quedius schatzmayri Gridelli	5		
Quedius tristis (Garvenhorst)	1		
Habrocerus capillaricornis (Gravenhorst)	1,3		
Lordithon lunulatus (Linnaeus)	5		
Sepedophilus marshami (Stephens)	1,2,3,4		
Sepedophilus nigripennis (Stephens)	1,3		
Sepedophilus testaceus (Fabricius)	5		
Tachyporus chrysomelinus (Linnaeus)	1,3		
Tachyporus dispar (Paykull)	1,3		
Tachyporus hypnorum (Fabricius)	1,3,5		
Tachyporus nitidulus (Fabricius)	1,2,3,4		
Tachyporus obtusus (Linnaeus)	1,3		

Tachyporus pallidus Sharp	3	
Tachyporus solutus Erichson	3	
Tachinus laticollis Gravenhorst	1,5	
Tachinus signatus Gravenhorst	1,2,3,5	
Cypha longicornis (Paykull)	1	
Oligota pumilio Kiesenwetter	3,5	
Gyrophaena affinis Mannerheim	5	
Gyrophaena bihamata Thomson	5	S
Leptusa fumida Kraatz	1	S
Leptusa ruficollis (Erichson)	2,5	S
Bolitochara bella Märkel	1	
Bolitochara lucida (Gravenhorst)	1	S
Autalia rivularis (Gravenhorst)	5	
Callicerus obscurus Gravenhorst	5	
Aloconota gregaria (Erichson)	3,5	
Amischa analis (Gravenhorst)	1,3,4,5	
Amischa decipiens (Sharp)	3	
Amischa nigrofusca (Stephens)	3	
Dinaraea aequata (Erichson)	1	S
Dinaraea angustula (Gyllenhal)	3	
Plataraea brunnea (Fabricius)	2	
Atheta amplicollis (Mulsant & Rey)	4,5	
Atheta aquatica (Thomson)	3	
Atheta atramentaria (Gyllenhal)	3	
Atheta clientula (Erichson)	3,4,5	
Atheta crassicornis (Fabricius)	5	
Atheta fungi (Gravenhorst)	3,4,5	
Atheta laticollis (Stephens)	1,3	
Atheta nigripes (Kraatz)	3	
Atheta orbata (Erichson)	3	
Atheta vilis (Erichson)	3	
Drusilla canaliculata (Fabricius)	3,4,5	
Chiloporata longitarsis (Erichson)	4	
Ocalea rivularis Miller	3	
Meotica apicalis (Benick)	3	
Oxypoda opaca (Gravenhorst)	1	
Haploglossa pulla (Gyllenhal)	1	
Aleochara funebris Wollaston	5	
Aleochara lanuginosa Gravenhorst	1	
Euplectus infirmus Raffray	5	S
Euplectus karsteni (Reichenbach)	5	S
LUCANIDAE		
Dorcus parallelipipedus (Linnaeus)	1,5	S
SCARABAEIDAE		
Aphodius ater (Degeer)	1	
Aphodius contaminatus (Herbst)	5	
Aphodius fimetarius (Linnaeus)	5	
Aphodius granarius (Linnaeus)	5	
Aphodius prodromus (Brahm)	5	

Aphodius sphacelatus (Panzer)	5		
CLAMBIDAE			
Clambus armadillo (Degeer)	3		
Clambus pubescens Redtenbacher	1		
SCIRTIDAE			
Cyphon coarctatus Paykull	2,4,5		
Cyphon variabilis (Thunberg)	1		
Prionocyphon serricornis (P.W.J. Müller)	5	S	Nb
BYRRHIDAE			
Byrrhus pilula (Linnaeus)	5		
BUPRESTIDAE			
Agrilus laticornis (Illiger)	5	S	Nb
ELATERIDAE			
Kibunea minuta (Linnaeus)	2,4		
Denticollis linearis (Linnaeus)	5	S	
Athous haemorrhoidalis (Fabricius)	1,2,4,5		
Stenagostus rhombeus (Olivier)	2	S	
Agriotes acuminatus (Stephens)	4,5		
Agriotes lineatus (Linnaeus)	5		
Agriotes pallidulus (Illiger)	2,5		
Agriotes sputator (Linnaeus)	3		
Melanotus villosus (Fourcroy)	1,2,5	S	
CANTHARIDAE			
Cantharis decipiens Baudi	4,5		
Cantharis nigricans (O.F. Müller)	1		
Cantharis pellucida Fabricius	1,4,5		
Cantharis rufa Linnaeus	5		
Cantharis rustica Fallén	5		
Rhagonycha limbata Thomson	1		
Malthodes minimus (Linnaeus)	1	S	
LAMPYRIDAE			
Lampyris noctiluca (Linnaeus)	5		
DERMESTIDAE			
Anthrenus museorum (Linaneus)	5		
Anthrenus verbasci (Linnaeus)	5		
ANOBIIDAE			
Ochina ptinoides (Marsham)	5	S	
Xestobium rufovillosum (Degeer)	5	S	
Hemicoelus fulvicornis (Sturm)	1,5	S	
Anobium punctatum (Degeer)	5	S	
Ptilinus pectinicornis (Linnaeus)	5	S	
Ptinus sexpunctatus Panzer	5	S	Nb
CLERIDAE			
Tillus elongatus (Linnaeus)	5	S	Nb
MELYRIDAE			
Dasytes aeratus Stephens	5	S	
Malachius bipustulatus (Linnaeus)	1	S	
BRACHYPTERIDAE			
Brachypterus glaber (Stephens)	2		

Brachypterus urticae (Fabricius)	1		
NITIDULIDAE			
Pria dulcamarae (Scopoli)	1		
Meligethes aeneus (Fabricius)	3,4,5		
Meligethes flavimanus Stephens	5		
Meligethes morosus Erichson	3		
Meligethes nigrescens Stephens	1,3		
Meligethes viridescens (Fabricius)	1		
Epuraea aestiva (Linnaeus)	1,2,4,5		
Epuraea deleta Sturm	5		
Epuraea melanocephala (Marsham)	3		
Epuraea unicolor (Olivier)	1,5		
Omosita discoidea (Fabricius)	4		
Pocadius ferrugineus (Fabricius)	5		
Cychramus luteus (Fabricius)	5		
Glischrochilus hortensis (Fourcroy)	5		
MONOTOMIDAE			
Rhizophagus bipustulatus (Fabricius)	5	S	
Rhizophagus dispar (Paykull)	1	S	
Monotoma picipes Herbst	1		
CRYPTOPHAGIDAE			
Telmatophilus caricis (Olivier)	1		
Paramecosoma melanocephalum (Herbst)	3		
Cryptophagus pallidus Sturm	5	S	
Cryptophagus pseudodentatus Bruce	1		
Antherophagus nigricornis (Fabricius)	5		
Atomaria apicalis Erichson	1		
Atomaria atricapilla Stephens	1,3		
Atomaria fuscata (Schoenherr)	3		
Atomaria nitidula (Marsham)	3		
Atomaria rubella Reitter	3		
Atomaria testacea Stephens	1,3		
Atomaria turgida Erichson	3		
Ephistemus globulus (Paykull)	3,5		
BIPHYLLIDAE			
Biphyllus lunatus (Fabricius)	3,4	S	
BYTURIDAE			
Byturus ochraceus (Scriba)	2,5		
Byturus tomentosus (Degeer)	1		
EROTYLIDAE			
Triplax russica (Linnaeus)	5	S	
Dacne bipustulata (Thunberg)	5	S	
Dacne rufifrons (Fabricius)	5	S	
PHALACRIDAE			
Stilbus testaceus (Panzer)	1,3		
CERYLONIDAE			
Cerylon histeroides (Fabricius)	1	S	
CORYLOPHIDAE			
Orthoperus nigrescens Stephens	5	S	**Nb**

COCCINELLIDAE

Subcoccinella 24-punctata (Linnaeus)	3,5		
Coccidula rufa (Herbst)	1,5		
Scymnus auritus Thunberg	1		
Scymnus suturalis Thunberg	2,4		
Exochomus 4-pustulatus (Linnaeus)	2,4		
Anisostica 19-punctata (Linnaeus)	1		
Aphidecta obliterata (Linnaeus)	5		
Tytthaspis 16-punctata (Linnaeus)	1,3		
Adalia bipunctata (Linnaeus)	2,3		
Adalia 10-punctata (Linnaeus)	1,2,3,5		
Coccinella 7-punctata Linnaeus	3,5		
Harmonia 4-punctata (Pontoppidan)	2		
Propylea 14-punctata (Linnaeus)	1,2		

ALEXIIDAE

Alexia piliferum (P.W.J. Müller)	1		

LATRIDIIDAE

Stephostethus lardarius (Degeer)	1		
Aridius bifasciatus (Reitter)	1,3		
Aridius nodifer (Westwood)	3,5		
Enicmus transversus (Olivier)	1,2,5		
Corticaria elongata (Gyllenhal)	1		
Corticaria impressa (Olivier)	3		
Corticaria punctulata Marsham	3,4		
Corticarina fuscula (Gyllenhal)	3		
Cortinicara gibbosa (Herbst)	1,2,3,4,5		

MYCETOPHAGIDAE

Mycetophagus multipunctatus Fabricius	5	S	
Mycetophagus 4-pustulatus (Linnaeus)	5	S	
Typhaea stercorea (Linnaeus)	1		

COLYDIIDAE

Bitoma crenata (Fabricius)	1,5	S	

TENEBRIONIDAE

Cylindronotus laevioctostriatus (Goeze)	5		
Scaphidema metallicum (Fabricius)	3	S	Nb
Lagria hirta (Linnaeus)	5		
Prionychus ater (Fabricius)	5	S	Nb
Pseudocistela ceramboides (Linnaeus)	5	S	Nb

SALPINGIDAE

Rhinosimus planirostris (Fabricius)	1,5	S	

PYROCHROIDAE

Pyrochroa serraticornis (Scopoli)	2,5	S	

MELANDRYIDAE

Orchesia undulata Kraatz	5	S	

SCRAPTIIDAE

Anaspis costai Emery	1	S	
Anaspis frontalis (Linnaeus)	5	S	
Anaspis humeralis (Fabricius)	2,5	S	
Anaspis lurida Stephens	5	S	

Anaspis maculata Fourcroy	1,2,4,5	S	
Anaspis pulicaria A. Costa	5	S	
Anaspis regimbarti Schilsky	5	S	
MORDELLIDAE			
Mordellistena abdominalis (Fabricius)	5	**S**	
OEDEMERIDAE			
Ischnomera cyanea (Fabricius)	4,5	**S**	**Nb**
Oedemera lurida (Marsham)	5		
Oedemera nobilis (Scopoli)	5		
CERAMBYCIDAE			
Rhagium mordax (Degeer)	5	S	
Stenocorus meridianus (Linnaeus)	5	S	
Grammoptera ruficornis (Fabricius)	1,2,4,5	S	
Anoplodera livida (Fabricius)	5	S	
Leptura maculata Poda	5	S	
Clytus arietis (Linnaeus)	5	S	
Leiopus nebulosus (Linnaeus)	5	S	
Phytoecia cylindrica (Linnaeus)	5		**Nb**
CHRYSOMELIDAE			
Bruchus atomarius (Linnaeus)	5		**Nb**
Bruchus rufipes Herbst	2		
Donacia simplex Fabricius	5		
Orsodacne cerasi (Linnaeus)	5		
Oulema melanopus (Linnaeus)	1		
Chrysolina polita (Linnaeus)	5		
Chrysolina staphylaea (Linnaeus)	5		
Phratora laticollis (Suffrian)	5		
Galeruca tanaceti (Linnaeus)	5		
Lochmaea crataegi (Forster)	4,5		
Phyllotreta nigripes (Fabricius)	3		
Aphthona euphorbiae (Schrank)	2		
Longitarsus kutscherae (Rye)	5		
Longitarsus parvulus (Paykull)	5		**Na**
Altica lythri Aubé	4,5		
Chalcoides aurata (Marsham)	3,5		
Chalcoides aurea (Fourcroy)	2,3,5		
Chalcoides plutus (Latreille)	3		
Epitrix pubescens (J.D.W. Koch)	1,5		
Chaetocnema concinna (Marsham)	1		
Chaetocnema hortensis (Fourcroy)	5		
Psylliodes affinis (Paykull)	1		
Psylliodes dulcamarae (J.D.W. Koch)	5		
Cassida rubiginosa O.F. Müller	1,5		
ATTELABIDAE			
Rhynchites aequatus (Linnaeus)	4		
Rhynchites caeruleus (Degeer)	4,5		
APIONIDAE			
Apion apricans Herbst	1		
Apion curtirostre Germar	1		

Apion ervi Kirby	1		
Apion hydrolapathi (Marsham)	1		
Apion simile Kirby	4		
Apion virens Herbst	5		
Apion vorax Herbst	1		
CURCULIONIDAE			
Otiorhynchus singularis (Linnaeus)	2		
Phyllobius glaucus (Scopoli)	5		
Phyllobius maculicornis Germar	1		
Phyllobius pomaceus Gyllenhal	1		
Phyllobius pyri (Linnaeus)	1,2,5		
Phyllobius roboretanus Gredler	1		
Polydrusus cervinus (Linnaeus)	5		
Polydrusus pterygomalis Boheman	1		
Barypeithes pellucidus (Boheman)	5		
Sitona lineatus (Linnaeus)	1,3,5		
Notaris acridulus (Linnaeus)	5		
Cionus scrophulariae (Linnaeus)	5		
Tanysphyrus lemnae (Paykull)	3		
Cossonus linearis (Fabricius)	2	**S**	**Na**
Euophryum confine (Broun)	5	**S**	
Phloeophagus lignarius (Marsham)	1	**S**	
Acalles misellus Boheman	5	**S**	
Cidnorhinus 4-maculatus (Linnaeus)	3,5		
Ceutorhynchus contractus (Marsham)	1		
Ceutorhynchus pollinarius (Forster)	5		
Ceutorhynchus quadridens (Panzer)	1,5		
Rhinoncus pericarpius (Linnaeus)	3		
Phytobius quadrituberculatus (Fabricius)	1		
Curculio glandium Marsham	2,5		
Gymnetron pascuorum (Gyllenhal)	5		
Rhynchaenus signifer (Creutzer)	5		
Rhynchaenus pilosus (Fabricius)	1,5		
Rhynchaenus quercus (Linnaeus)	1,5		
Scolytus intricatus (Ratzeburg)	5	**S**	
Scolytus scolytus (Fabricius)	5	**S**	
Hylesinus varius (Fabricius)	2	**S**	

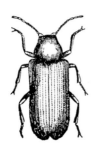

Xestobium rufovillosum

Veteran Trees and Saproxylic Invertebrates at Hylands

Mark Hanson

Introduction

Over the last 25 years in Britain there has been a growing awareness of the importance of wood-pasture sites and their mature, old and ancient trees (veteran trees) and the contribution they make to the conservation needs of a significant percentage of the fauna and flora of the British Isles. So-called 'saproxylic invertebrates' are those species that depend on wood, usually but not always, dead and decaying, for some part of their life-cycle.

It is estimated that there are probably at least 1,700 species that fall into this category in Britain, the vast majority being flies (Diptera) and beetles (Coleoptera). They include species that feed on wood in its various stages from solid to completely decayed, often with a single species exploiting a particular niche at any one stage. The term also encompasses those that live on associated fungi, on sap-runs, in rot-holes (of many types, wet and dry), under bark and those species that predate or parasitise these saproxylic species.

Often a beetle or a fly will occupy a very specific niche in an old tree – a hundred trees each fifty years old, are no substitute for a single tree 500 years old and similarly, a diverse age range of trees from one to 500 years old is much more desirable than a two or three hundred year old gap in the age distribution of a group of veteran trees, giving a continuity of habitat over a long period of time. Many saproxylic invertebrates seem to have poor powers of dispersal – particularly some beetles – and so it is that many species have collectively come to be used as indicator species for habitat quality and stability.

The U.K. makes a significant contribution to the population of veteran trees in north-west Europe. It has been noted on many occasions, that there are relatively few very ancient trees to be seen on mainland Europe (north of the Pyrenees). It is not until one reaches the U.K. that veteran trees become at all frequent. However, despite this, the U.K. saproxylic fauna is thought to be impoverished, compared to some European countries (ie France and Austria), probably due to post-glacial isolation and later forest (wild-wood) clearance for agriculture with its associated fragmentation. Climate almost certainly plays a part – for example the mainly tropical jewel beetles (Buprestidae) have some 100 species recorded in Europe; the damp, cold Atlantic climate is not to their liking and just 12 species are recorded in Britain. Of these, just one species has been recorded at Hylands, the nationally notable *Agrilus laticornis*. The general scarcity of over-mature trees indicates that many saproxylics are considered to be amongst the rarest invertebrates in Europe.

Evaluation of Wood-Pasture Sites

Because of their often very restricted occurrence, limited powers of dispersal and generally the isolation of the particular site a saproxylic species occurs in, they have come to be used as indicator species – enabling conservation workers to grade and rank a particular site for its conservation significance. Various methods using different criteria have been used, mostly involving known indicator species that have been given a simple scoring – for example on a three-point scale to show how strong is that species' association with the wood-pasture/old forest habitat. As a result of such surveys, the Nature Conservancy Council (now English Nature) introduced the Invertebrate

Site Register. Later developments included the Index of Ecological Continuity and the Saproxylic Quality Index, which used the rarity status of species recorded to achieve a figure which could then be used to place a particular site in a ranked order.

The European Context

In 1989 the Council of Europe published a report – 'Saproxylic Invertebrates and their Conservation' – by Dr Martin Speight. In this report, Speight attempted to evaluate the conservation significance of European wood-pasture/old forest sites using saproxylic invertebrates as bio-indicators of habitat quality. His list of indicator species, which he thought could be useful in identifying sites of international importance, included the following four species:

Ischnomera cyanea (Coleoptera : Oedemeridae)

Callicera aurata (Diptera : Syrphidae)

Callicera spinolae (Diptera : Syrphidae)

Psilota anthracina (Diptera : Syrphidae)

These four species have all been recorded at Hylands Park in the last two years, all four being noted from the formal gardens area.

Trees at Hylands

Hylands has a great diversity of both native and planted trees. As a later landscaped park, the treescape is dominated by standard trees (not pollards) some – particularly the oaks – are now of an impressive size. The park also has a few pollards, coppice stools and bundle-plantings. The park is also correspondingly rich in habitats for saproxylic species (dead-wood, sap-runs, rot-holes, fungi, etc). Of note is the large amount of dead-wood to be found about the park.

Other important factors for trees is that the ground around the trees is not ploughed (although the northern part of the park around Swan Pond was cultivated until the 1990s), which means there is no disturbance to the root-plates of the trees. Also, there is no application of herbicide, fungicide, or insecticide in the vicinity of the trees – important for invertebrates and particularly for the fungus species that inhabit the root-zones of the trees. As a result of this, despite the ageing population of standard oaks, the trees at Hylands are actually in generally very good tree health.

Another factor for trees at Hylands is that there is no Bracken (*Pteridium aquilinum*) invasion, unlike some very acid wood-pasture sites, such as Epping Forest, the New Forest, or Moccas Park, where is has become an invasive pest species which, when dry, becomes flammable and can damage some older trees. Some parks and forests have had tree regeneration significantly checked by periods of heavy grazing by domestic stock or deer. Hylands has been grazed by domestic stock, chiefly cattle and sheep, but also horses and is currently grazed and browsed by a herd of around a hundred Fallow Deer and some Muntjac, but noticeably not enough to check regeneration – some palatable species, such as Ash, surviving well. There is also no evidence of a browse-line which characterises many over-grazed wood-pasture sites.

Trees at Hylands – Notable Dates

1808 Planted fir trees near the Hylands lodge gate wilfully destroyed (Essex Herald – January 1808).

1855 Proposal to fell 125 oak trees in the park by Sadds of Maldon was thwarted by an injunction granted to a Thomas Howard, presumably a creditor of the then owner John Attwood (ERO, D/ DDW/B5/5).

1978 £4,000 tree planting grant, resulting in some 2000 trees being planted. Part of South Wood planted (Foreman, 1999).

1987 October storm fells many trees in the park, including conifers in the Lake Plantation and numerous large oaks, the formal gardens taking a month to clear of fallen trees (Foreman, 1999).

Hylands as a site for Saproxylic Invertebrates

To date a minimum of 150 saproxylic fly and beetle have been recorded at Hylands. This list is a minimum because it is certain that other species whose life history is unknown or unrecorded, will turn out to be saproxylics. The lists also do not include the many invertebrate species from other groups, such as spiders, woodlice, 'myriapods', moths, etc., which can also be legitimately accorded saproxylic status. The dominant group is the Coleoptera (79 species recorded) with Diptera (71 species recorded) following. With other saproxylics it is likely that around 10% of the known British saproxylic fauna is found at Hylands.

Hylands differs greatly from other wood-pasture sites in Essex, its boundary encompassing some 570 acres (237.5 ha.) is relatively recent when compared to Epping and Hatfield Forests, which were both established entities in the medieval period. Hylands was established as a small c.100 acres (41.7 ha.) estate in about 1730 carved out of an existing agricultural landscape, including pasture, meadows, hedgerows, coppiced woodland and probably some acid grassland (or heath). By 1777 (see map) a small c.100 acre park was established here. The Chapman and Andre map indicates that this core part of Hylands was indeed a wood-pasture estate, with coppiced woodland, pasture and mature trees, the whole being surrounded by a pale. The park was added to greatly over the succeeding two centuries, eventually becoming the 570 acre park we see today. Recording, particularly the beetle fauna, seems to underline the general premise that parks created in the 17th – 19th centuries have been colonised by few of the more specialised saproxylic species that are found at more ancient sites, such as forests and medieval deer parks.

Pollard Trees

One of the defining elements of any wood-pasture site is its pollard trees. Trees were pollarded, that is cut at usually 8 – 10ft (2.44m – 3.05m) above ground level to prevent livestock from browsing the re-growth. The wood cut was used for various products from pea sticks to hedging stakes, but the majority for firewood.

Pollard trees are very important to saproxylic invertebrates for a variety of reasons, the main ones being they are long-lived - pollarding almost indefinitely prolongs the life of a tree (some of the giant pollard oaks of Windsor Forest are possibly 8 or 900 years old). As a consequence of this, they can provide a very stable habitat over periods of many hundreds of years, important for the survival of many plants and animals. A third factor is that as they age, they often develop heart-rot and dead-wood within the tree itself, whilst the outer shell still lives. This is exploited by saproxylic invertebrates which would otherwise be hard-pressed to find dead wood, for example in a coppice-wood where every piece of wood was utilised and the trees felled before maturity.

In wood-pastures too, fallen wood would be collected and used for fuel. This situation is well-shown in medieval Havering, where numerous grants were made, to mainly religious establishments, of dead wood for fuel in the 13th century from the park, woodland outside the park and also from Hainault Forest. In about 1650, when Havering was about to be disparked and sold, its trees were described thus "being only white-thorn, pollards and old dottrells, fit for firing only, besides what is marked for the use of the Navy" (ie the standard trees for building ships with).

In a deer park of medieval origin (such as Staverton Park, Suffolk or Weald Park), or indeed an ancient royal forest with a strong tradition of common wood-cutting rights (such as Epping Forest) there can usually be found substantial numbers of ancient pollard trees – Staverton Park has some 4,000 in a 200 acre (85ha.) park. Hatfield Forest, at 1,000 acres (416 ha.) has around 800, whilst Epping Forest is thought to have probably 72,000 in 6,000 acres (2,500 ha.). Hylands lacking, for example, the long historic continuity of these sites and also common wood-cutting rights as found in Epping Forest, has far fewer pollard trees.

In 2003 I surveyed the pollard trees at Hylands and found a total of just 64 individuals of the following species:

Oak (*Quercus robur*)	35
Hornbeam (*Carpinus betulus*)	11
Horse Chestnut (*Aesculus hippocastanum*)	11
Sycamore (*Acer pseudoplatanus*)	4
Ash (*Fraxinus excelsior*)	1
Beech (*Fagus sylvatica*)	1 (storm-felled 2001)
Lime (*Tilia* x *vulgaris*)	1
	———
Total:	**64 pollards**
	———

The oaks are all boundary pollards from hedgerows incorporated into the park, mainly in the 19th century. The largest of these trees, also with the largest girth of any tree in the park, is the Great Oak on Writtle Hills. This tree has a girth of just over 20ft (6.11m) and it significantly pre-dates the establishment of the park. It may well be over 500 years old, possibly originating in the very late medieval period. Many of the other pollard oaks have girths in the range 11ft to 19ft (3.35m – 5.83m) and most are probably over 300 years old. Most of the pollard oaks are still in good tree health, though a few have conspicuous 'Ganoderma' bracket fungi and one or two are stag-headed. The eleven Hornbeam pollards are also mostly on old boundaries – particularly noticeable along the Lower Belt (the southern boundary of Hylands) and also on the fragment of ancient wood bank just south of the junction of South Wood with the Tower Belt. The finest Hornbeam pollard is undoubtedly the great, gnarled, holed, wrinkled old veteran (girth 13ft 2ins – 4.0m) just west of the Home Farm plantation. Such a tree, although not particularly large in girth, is probably well over 400 years old.

The remaining 18 pollards are almost certainly more recent in origin, being trees planted and subsequently pollarded in the 18th century as part of various landscaping schemes. Notable trees include the giant Horse Chestnut (girth 18ft 6.5ins – 5.65m) and the probably bundle-planted Ash (girth 19ft 5.5ins – 5.93m).

Locations and girth of some of the more notable pollard trees are given below (girthed at 1.3m):

Oak (*Quercus robur*) Pollards

Football Field	TL 67989 04646	14ft 9ins	4.5m
Writtle Hills	TL 68010 04648	15ft	4.58m
Nr Pond Plantation	TL 68451 03449	15ft 8ins	4.76m
Nr Pigeon Plantation	TL 68068 03928	19ft 2ins	5.83m
Writtle Hills (Great Oak)	TL 68082 04545	20ft 1ins	6.11m

Hornbeam (*Carpinus betulus*) Pollards

Nr Writtle Wood	TL 68300 04630	9ft 4ins	2.8m
Nr Pond Plantation	TL 68335 03468	11ft 3ins	3.42m
Nr Home Farm Plantation	TL 68078 04164	13ft 2ins	4.0m

Horse Chestnut (*Aesculus hippocastanum*) Pollard

Lake Field Boundary	TL 68503 04848	18ft 6.5ins	5.65m

Ash (*Fraxinus excelsior*) Pollard

Nr Ice House Plantation (Possible bundle-planting)	TL 68850 04448	19ft 5.5ins	5.93m

Sycamore (*Acer pseudoplatanus*) Pollard

Formal Gardens	TL 68564 04259	11ft 6.5ins	3.51m

This lack of pollard trees, when compared to other sites, probably partly accounts for the rather (as far as is known) limited saproxylic beetle fauna. Notably, no Red Data Book beetles have been found at Hylands. Flies with a number of RDB species recorded at Hylands, mostly rare saproxylics, are more mobile than beetles and may be less confined to a particular site than the corresponding beetle fauna. Despite the paucity of pollard trees, Hylands is, however, a notable site for its sizeable standard trees, some two-thirds of which are oak (Quercus robur). I estimated the population of large standard oaks (girths 10ft = 3.05m and over) at around 200 in 2003, with many hundreds in the 6ft (1.83m) and over category. There are substantial numbers of very large standard oaks in the

13ft – 17ft (3.96m – 5.18m) girth category (see sample list). Other species that make a contribution to the population of significant standard trees, include Horse Chestnut, Lime (Tilia x vulgaris), Ash, Plane (few), Sycamore, Beech (rather few), with Pine (Pinus sylvestris) and Yew in the formal gardens.

The vast majority of the largest oaks probably date from the period 1600 to 1800. The oldest tree ring count I made was 326 years in a standard oak felled by the 1987 storm. This tree had a girth of 13ft 8ins (4.15m) and would have started life in about 1660. Of a number of felled oaks to have had their rings counted, I found a great variability bearing little relation to the actual girth of the tree. A tree with a girth of 15ft (4.57m) had 256 annual rings. Another with a girth of 12ft 5ins (3.77m) had 284 annual rings and yet another of girth 7ft 10ins (2.38m) had 148 annual rings.

Many of the old standard oaks, like the pollards, are on old hedgerow boundaries, the best example being the 10 or so trees in alignment between the Margaretting Gate and Oak Plantation. The grove of 27 very large standard oaks (largest tree 16ft 11.5ins = 5.17m) opposite the entrance to the Stable Block is something of a puzzle, but I suspect they originated as the standard trees in a coppice wood which subsequently had its coppice stools removed and boundary bank flattened as part of a landscaping scheme. Chapman and Andre (1777) show coppiced woodland in approximately the right position.

SOME NOTABLE STANDARD TREES

Oak (*Quercus robur*) (girthed at 1.3m)

Formal Gardens	TL 68324 04290	13ft 3ins	4.03m
Formal Gardens	TL 68412 04416	13ft 9ins	4.18m
Lake Field	TL 68817 04609	14ft 9.5ins	4.49m
By Writtle Gate	TL 68087 05255	15ft 3ins	4.64m
Writtle Hills	TL 68120 04522	15ft 8ins	4.76m
Lake Field	TL 68649 04475	16ft 5ins	5.01m
Formal Gardens	TL 68341 04436	16ft 8ins	5.08m
Nr Main Gate	TL 68759 04219	16ft 10.5ins	5.15m
Nr Stable Block	TL 68382 04166	16ft 11.5ins	5.17m

There is a good age range of standard oaks in the park. However, this tends to be very uneven in distribution around the park – the largest trees are to be found due east of the house, south of the Stable Block and in the Writtle Hills area. The formal gardens has some 20 trees with girths over 8ft (2.44m) and a few notably larger in the 13ft – 16ft (3.96m – 4.88m) bracket. Lightfoot Spring has probably a similar number of suspiciously uniform looking standard oaks of girth 6ft – 9ft

(1.83m – 2.74m), possibly planted with timber production in mind. There is also a fine standard Ash here.

Most of the standard oak trees are apparently in good health – though they do harbour some (sometimes rare) species of bracket fungi, such as *Ganoderma resinaceum, Inonotus dryadeus, Grifola frondosa* and the edible species *Fistulina hepatica* and *Laetiporous sulphureus. Fistulina* (beef-steak fungus) causes red-rot in oak, which is important for beetles such as the rare *Pseudocistela ceramboides*, so far known from only one tree at Hylands. It is likely that standard trees do not harbour such a good saproxylic beetle fauna as pollard trees. However, rot-holes, shattered branch ends from storms, much dead wood where whole branches have split-off from the trunk, rarely sap-runs, red and white-rot, plus dead branches high up in the tree (home to species such as *Scolytus intricatus*) mean that standard oaks at Hylands do have the potential to provide at least some sort of habitat for saproxylic species.

Trees Other Than Oak

Of the other tree species in the park, the most important for saproxylic species is probably the Horse Chestnut (*Aesculus hippocastanum*) which was obviously widely planted in the 19th century (and possibly earlier). This species is a good example of how a non-native tree can become a good site for invertebrates, providing many of the niches that would normally be found only in much older native trees. The large pollard tree near the western end of the Serpentine Lake (girth 18ft 6.5ins – 5.65m) is on part of the estate acquired by Cornelius Kortright after 1797, so the tree was probably planted some 200 years ago (Horse Chestnuts make sizeable trees relatively quickly). This tree has sap-runs oozing out of folds in the trunk and also in one of its larger branches. It also has a sizeable wet rot-hole at its base full of decaying wood and with an internal sap-run. It also has rot-holes in the main trunk, dead wood, accumulations of wet leaves caught in buttressing at the trunk base and also has a *Ganoderma* bracket fungus at its base. The following saproxylic flies have been recorded on this tree:

Aulacigaster leucopeza
Brachyopa insensilis
Brachypalpoides lentus
Criorhina ranunculi

Ferdinandea cuprea
Mycetobia pallipes
Xylota xanthocnema
Systenus pallipes

Brachyopa insensilis and *Aulacigaster leucopeza* have been found on numerous Horse Chestnut sap-runs in the park, particularly in the formal gardens. Even quite small trees can provide useful habitat. I have found a well-developed rot-hole in a tree with a girth of just 20 inches (51cms), another Horse Chestnut with its trunk shattered by the 1987 storms at 2ft (61cms) above ground level and with re-growth around the rim shading a well-rotted and leaf-filled interior has provided two reared records of the nationally notable beetle *Prionocyphon serricornis* and the fly *Systenus scholtzii*. The two Red Data Book flies *Callicera spinolae* and *Callicera aurata* have also both been reared from rot-holes in Horse Chestnut at Wimpole Hall in Cambridgeshire (but other species are recorded as well) and it is likely that these two species are using some of the many suitable Horse Chestnuts in and around the formal gardens area. *Criorhina ranunculi* found new to Essex at Hylands is another species I noted around decaying parts on the lower trunk of Horse Chestnuts.

Beech (*Fagus sylvatica*) is a significant and important tree for saproxylic species at places such as Epping Forest, Windsor Forest and Burnham Beeches, where it is probably native and found in numbers. This is not the case at Hylands, where it is found only in very small quantity and all are planted. Of the dozen or so large trees (mainly in the Writtle Belt) at least 9 are dead (including one of the copper beech trees in the formal gardens). The dead trees would probably be worth investigating for their beetles and at least one dead tree has the ant *Lasius brunneus* nesting in it. Beech does not seem to thrive at Hylands, but new trees have been planted in some of the plantations, presumably in the 1970s.

Ash (*Fraxinus excelsior*) is again rather scarce as a large standard tree. The old, possibly bundle-planted pollard has provided the only record of the scarce weevil (*Cossonus linearis*) for Essex. There are two very large, hollow standards – one near the Ice-House Plantation has a girth of 15ft 8ins (4.76m). Both trees would repay investigation for their beetle (and probably bat) inhabitants. Other large standard Ash trees occur in Writtle Wood and Lightfoot Spring. Some sizeable Ash coppice stools occur in parts of South Wood.

Some of the Hawthorns (*Crataegus monogyna*) in Roman Walk are now sizeable specimens. They probably originated as bundle-plantings in the late 19th century. These thorns have provided a record of the scarce Red-belted Clearwing Moth (*Synanthedon myopaeiformis*).

Standard Trees – Native and Non-Native – Girthed at 1.3m

Ash (*Fraxinus excelsior*) Nr Ice House Plantation	TL 68784 04320	15ft 8ins	4.78m
Nr Writtle Wood	TL 68353 04761	11ft 6ins	3.51m
Maple (*Acer campestre*) Writtle Wood	TL 68274 04717	5ft 5ins	1.64m
Sweet Chestnut (*Castanea sativa*) Rook Plantation	TL 68406 03904	8ft 4ins	2.53m
Alder (*Alnus glutinosa*) Formal Gardens	TL 68374 04364	11ft 1ins	3.37m
Scots Pine (*Pinus sylvestris*) Formal Gardens	TL 68365 04325	6ft 7ins	2.00m
Yew (*Taxus baccata*) Formal Gardens	TL 68414 04296	9ft 2ins	2.78m
Wellingtonia (*Sequoiadendron giganteum*) Formal Gardens	TL 68343 04428	16ft 4ins\	4.98m
Black Walnut (*Juglans nigra*) Formal Gardens	TL 68533 04283	13ft 5ins	3.43m
Walnut (*Juglans regia*) By East Wall	TL 68929 04360	9ft 11ins	3.01m
Pyrenean Oak (*Quercus pyrenaica*)* Nr Lightfoot Spring	TL 68048 03753	10ft 7ins	3.21m
Wild Crab (*Malus sylvestris*) Nr South Wood	TL 67913 04218	6ft 4ins	1.92m

*This is probably the largest Pyrenean Oak in England.

Dead Wood

Hylands is one of the best dead-wood sites in Essex. The 'tidy-minded' approach to park management practised by some local authorities has not happened at Hylands. This has resulted in a superb site for decaying wood and its associated invertebrates. The range of fallen dead wood is considerable, from the tiniest branches of Lime and Cherry to mightly trunks of Oak four feet in diameter. The violent storms that have been a notable feature of many recent autumns have left their mark. There are still dozens of decaying conifer trunks in the Lake Plantation, home now to the lovely black crane-fly *Dictenidia bimaculata*. Many large oak boughs and branches are also to be found, often fortuitously moved from where they fell to the shade directly underneath the trees, such branches often leaving a shattered end in the crown of the tree, making a good site for beetle and fungus entry. The variety of species of dead wood is also of note, though probably not as important as the stage of decay to many saproxylics. Oak is the dominant dead wood, but other species include Lime, Walnut, Beech, Horse Chestnut, Pine and Sycamore, with much decaying Birch in South Wood. Some Poplar trunks from trees felled in Central Park were deposited at the north end of Swan Pond plantation and this has provided the only record of the notable fly *Solva marginata*.

Nectar Sources

Another feature that has contributed to the success of Hylands Park as a site for saproxylic invertebrates, has been the supply of nectar-bearing shrubs and trees. In contrast to other sites, such as Moccas Park, Herefordshire – where Hawthorn has had to be planted as a supplementary nectar source for saproxylics – Hylands, because of its many plantings (native and ornamental) in particular in the vicinity of the formal gardens and nearby Writtle Wood and Home Farm – there is an almost constant and probably inexhaustible supply from many species of nectar-bearing shrubs and trees. The list of shrubs below, all from this area, are in flower from late February to July – some only with very few individuals, such as Blackthorn and Sallow, but others such as Cherry Laurel in quantity. Hawthorn also flowers in substantial amounts throughout the park.

Flowering trees and shrubs found in the vicinity of the formal gardens, Home Farm and Writtle Wood (in approximate flowering order):

Prunus cerasifera	*Aesculus hippocastanum*
Salix caprea	*Crataegus crus-galli*
Prunus laurocerasus	*Acer pseudo platanus*
Prunus padus	*Rhododendron* (*ponticum* + hybrids)
Prunus avium	*Prunus lusitanica*
Prunus (Ornamental Cherry)	*Pyracantha* (Firethorn)
Prunus spinosa	*Rubus fruticosus* agg.
Crataegus monogyna	*Philadelphus coronarius*

The Formal Gardens as a site for Saproxylic Invertebrates

The formal gardens, covering just sixteen or so acres, are outstanding and one of the most important sites for saproxylic invertebrates in Essex, with 13 nationally notable and 3 Red Data Book species amongst those recorded here in the years 2001 – 2003. I suspect that the gardens, with their abundant and continuous nectar sources, large standard Oak trees (and others, such as Lime and Horse Chestnut), much dead wood – particularly the trunks of trees felled in the 1987 storm which are slowly decaying in the dense shade of the abundant Cherry Laurel, interspersed with open expanses of lawn and flower bed, have helped to create an ideal environment for saproxylic species. The area as a whole – which mimics the old forest conditions and probably enhances them as well – suits this particular group of invertebrates.

Saproxylic Invertebrates recorded in the formal gardens 2001 – 2003

DIPTERA		COLEOPTERA	
Aulacigaster leucopeza		*Agrilus laticornis*	Nb
Brachyopa insensilis	N	*Anobium punctatum*	
Brachyopa scutellaris		*Bitoma crenata*	
Brachypalpoides lentus		*Dacne bipustulata*	
Callicera spinolae	RDB 1	*Dorcus parallelopipedus*	
Callicera aurata	RDB 3	*Ischnomera cyanea*	Nb
Choerades marginatus	N	*Leiopus nebulosus*	
Criorhina berberina		*Melanotus villosus*	
Criorhina floccosa		*Orchesia undulata*	
Criorhina ranunculi	N	*Orthoperus nigrescens*	Nb
Macrocera crassicornis	N	*Prionocyphon serricornis*	Nb
Megamerina dolium	N	*Ptilinus pectinicornis*	
Psilota anthracina	RDB 2	*Ptinus sexpunctatus*	Nb
Systenus scholtzii	N	*Rhagium mordax*	
Tipula flavolineata		*Tillus elongatus*	Nb
Xylota xanthocnema	N	*Xestobium rufovillosum*	

Distribution of some saproxylic hoverflies in Essex Parks

*   = present
** = found outside park boundary

	DAGNAM	HYLANDS	THORNDON	WEALD
Brachyopa insensilis	*	*	*	*
Brachyopa scutellaris	*	*	*	*
Brachypalpoides lentus	**	*	*	
Callicera aurata		*		
Callicera spinolae		*		
Chalcosyrphus nemorum	*	*	*	
Criorhina asilica		*	*	
Criorhina berberina		*		
Criorhina floccosa	*	*	*	
Criorhina ranunculi		*		
Didea fasciata		*		
Epistrophe diaphana		*		
Ferdinandea cuprea	*	*		
Ferdinandea ruficornis	**			
Mallota cimbiciformis				*
Meligramma euchroma	*			
Myolepta dubia	*	*		*
Psilota anthracina	*	*	*	*
Xylota sylvarum	*	*	*	*
Xylota xanthocnema		*		

References

Foreman, S. (1999) Hylands – the story of an Essex country house and its owners, 2nd ed. Ian Henry Publications

Harding, P.T. and Rose, F. (1986) Pasture-Woodlands in Lowland Britain – a review of their importance for wildlife conservation. Institute of Terrestrial Ecology

Harding, P.T and Wall, T. (2000) Moccas: an English deer park. English Nature

Kirby, K.J. and Drake, C.M. (1993) Dead Wood Matters: the ecology and conservation of saproxylic invertebrates in Britain. English Nature (Science No. 7)

Read, H.J. (2000) Veteran Trees – a guide to good management. English Nature

Smith, H. (1925) A History of the Parish of Havering-atte-Bower, Essex. (L.B. Havering reprint 1990)

Stubbs, A.E. and Chandler, P.J. (1978) A Dipterist's Handbook. The Amateur Entomologist Vol. 15. The Amateur Entomologists Society

Stubbs, A.E. and Falk, S.J. (2002) British Hoverflies – an illustrated identification guide. The British Entomological and Natural History Society

Hymenoptera : Aculeata from Hylands Park

Recorders : P.R.Harvey and M.W.Hanson

Essex statuses and their definitions are given in the provisional Essex Red Data list at
www.essexfieldclub.org.uk/ERDlist/ERDB.htm

Records: 2001 – 2002

	National status	Essex Rarity Status	Essex Threat Status
CHRYSIDIDAE			
Hedychridium roseum		Rare	Threatened
Chrysis angustula			
FORMICIDAE			
Myrmica rubra			
Myrmica ruginodis		Ubiquitous	
Myrmica scabrinodis			
Leptothorax nylanderi			
Lasius brunneus	Na	Scarce	Regionally Important
Lasius mixtus		Scarce	
Lasius niger			
POMPILIDAE			
Dipogon subintermedius		Scarce	
Priocnemis perturbator		Scarce	
Agenioideus cinctellus		Scarce	
EUMENIDAE			
Odynerus spinipes		Scarce	
Ancistrocerus parietinus		Rare	
Ancistrocerus trifasciatus		Scarce	
Symmorphus gracilis		Rare	Threatened
VESPIDAE			
Vespa crabro			
Dolichovespula media	Na	Scarce	
Dolichovespula saxonica	RDBK	Rare	
Vespula rufa		Rare	
Vespula germanica			
Vespula vulgaris			
SPHECIDAE			
Astata boops		Rare	Threatened
Trypoxylon attenuatum			
Trypoxylon clavicerum			
Crossocerus annulipes		Scarce	
Crossocerus megacephalus		Scarce	
Crossocerus podagricus		Scarce	
Crossocerus quadrimaculatus		Scarce	
Crossocerus pusillus		Scarce	
Ectemnius cavifrons		Scarce	
Ectemnius cephalotes		Scarce	
Lindenius albilabris			
Rhopalum clavipes		Scarce	

	National status	Essex Rarity Status	Essex Threat Status
SPHECIDAE cont.			
Stigmus pendulus	RDBK	Scarce	Regionally Important
Passaloecus corniger		Scarce	
Argogorytes mystaceus		Scarce	
COLLETIDAE			
Hylaeus communis			
ANDRENIDAE			
Andrena bicolor			
Andrena chrysoceles			
Andrena dorsata			
Andrena flavipes			
Andrena fulva			
Andrena helvola		Scarce	
Andrena haemorrhoa			
Andrena labiata	Na	Scarce	Threatened
Andrena nigroaenea			
Andrena scotica			
Andrena subopaca		Scarce	
Andrena varians	Nb	Scarce	Regionally Important
HALICTIDAE			
Halictus rubicundus			
Lasioglossum malachurum	Nb	Common	
Lasioglossum leucopus		Scarce	
Lasioglossum pauxillum	Na	Scarce	Regionally Important
Sphecodes ephippius			
Sphecodes geofrellus (=*fasciatus*)			
MEGACHILIDAE			
Megachile ligniseca		Scarce	
Chelostoma florisomne		Scarce	
Osmia rufa			
ANTHOPHORIDAE			
Nomada flava/panzeri			
Nomada flavoguttata			
Nomada ruficornis			
Anthophora plumipes			
APIDAE			
Apis mellifera			
Bombus barbutellus			
Bombus hortorum			
Bombus lapidarius			
Bombus lucorum			
Bombus pascuorum			
Bombus pratorum			
Bombus terrestris			
Bombus vestalis			

Bombus lapidarius

Arachnida : Araneae from Hylands Park

Recorders : P.R.Harvey and M.W.Hanson

The checklist followed is Merrett & Murphy (2000) A revised check list of British spiders. *Bull. Br. Arachnol. Soc.* **11** (9): 345-358. Essex statuses and their definitions are given in the provisional Essex Red Data list at www.essexfieldclub.org.uk/ERDlist/ERDB.htm

Records : 1988 and 2000 – 2003

	National Status	Essex Rarity Status	Essex Threat Status
PHOLCIDAE			
Pholcus phalangioides		Scarce	
MIMETIDAE			
Ero cambridgei			
THERIDIIDAE			
Achaearanea tepidariorum		Rare	
Anelosimus vittatus			
Enoplognatha ovata			
Robertus lividus			
Theridion bimaculatum			
Theridion pallens			
Theridion sisyphium			
Theridion tinctum			
Theridion varians			
LINYPHIIDAE			
Bathyphantes gracilis			
Bathyphantes nigrinus			
Bathyphantes parvulus			
Centromerita bicolor			
Diplostyla concolor			
Dismodicus bifrons			
Dicymbium brevisetosum		Scarce	
Erigone atra			
Floronia bucculenta		Scarce	
Gangylidium rufipes			
Hypomma cornutum		Scarce	
Labulla thoracica		Scarce	
Lepthyphantes alacris		Scarce	
Lepthyphantes ericaeus			
Lepthyphantes flavipes			
Lepthyphantes obscurus		Scarce	
Lepthyphantes tenuis			
Lepthyphantes zimmermanni			
Linyphia clathrata			
Linyphia hortensis			
Linyphia peltata			
Linyphia triangularis			
Macrargus rufus			

	National Status	Essex Rarity Status	Essex Threat Status
LINYPHIIDAE cont.			
Maso sundevalli			
Meioneta innotabilis		Scarce	
Micrargus herbigradus			
Microneta viaria			
Moebelia penicillata		Scarce	
Oedothorax retusus			
Thyreosthenius parasiticus		Scarce	
Walckenaeria acuminata			
Walckenaeria antica			
Walckenaeria unicornis			
TETRAGNATHIDAE			
Metellina mengei			
Metellina merianae			
Metellina segmentata			
Pachygnatha clercki			
Pachygnatha degeeri			
Tetragnatha montana			
Tetragnatha obtusa			
ARANEIDAE			
Agalenatea redii		Scarce	
Araneus diadematus			
Araniella opisthographa			
Cyclosa conica		Scarce	
Larinioides cornutus			
Neoscona adianta			
Nuctenea umbratica			
Zilla diodia	Nb	Local	Regionally Important
Zygiella atrica			
LYCOSIDAE			
Alopecosa pulverulenta			
Pardosa amentata			
Pardosa lugubris			
Pardosa prativaga			
Pardosa pullata			
Trochosa terricola			
PISAURIDAE			
Pisaura mirabilis			
AGELENIDAE			
Cicurina cicur		Scarce	
Tegenaria gigantea			
DICTYNIDAE			
Dictyna arundinacea			
AMAUROBIIDAE			
Amaurobius ferox		Scarce	
CLUBIONIDAE			
Clubiona brevipes			
Clubiona compta			

	National Status	Essex Rarity Status	Essex Threat Status
Clubiona lutescens			
Clubiona reclusa			
Clubiona terrestris			
Cheiracanthium erraticum			
ANYPHAENIDAE			
Anyphaena accentuata			
ZORIDAE			
Zora spinimana			
THOMISIDAE			
Diaea dorsata		Scarce	
Xysticus cristatus			
Xysticus ulmi			
PHILODROMIDAE			
Philodromus aureolus			
Philodromus albidus	Nb	Local	Regionally Important
Philodromus dispar			
Philodromus praedatus	Nb	Local	Regionally Important
Tibellus oblongus			
SALTICIDAE			
Ballus chalybeius		Scarce	
Heliophanus cupreus		Scarce	
Marpissa muscosa	Nb	Rare	Threatened
Pseudeuophrys lanigera			
Sitticus pubescens		Scarce	

Arachnida : Opiliones from Hylands Park

Recorder : P.R.Harvey

Records : 1988

Leiobunum blackwalli
Mitostoma chrysomelas
Nemastoma bimaculatum
Oligolophus tridens
Paraligolophus agrestis
Rilaena triangularis

Arachnida : Pseudoscorpiones from Hylands Park

Recorders : M.W. Hanson and P.R.Harvey

Records : 2000-2003

Allochernes wideri
Chthonius ischnocheles

Miscellaneous Invertebrates

Recorders: M.W.Hanson, Peter Harvey, the late Stan Hudgell, Jerry Bowdrey, Tim Gardiner, Dr Peter Kirby

Records: 2000 – 2003 (except gall-causing organisms)

MOLLUSCA (terrestrial)
Acanthinula aculeata
Aegopinella nitidula
Arion ater
Arion distinctus
Arion intermedius
Arion subfuscus
Carychium minimum
Carychium tridentatum
Cepaea nemoralis
Cochlicopa lubrica
Deroceras laeve
Deroceras reticulatum
Discus rotundatus
Ena obscura
Euconulus fulvus
Helix aspersa
Lauria cylindracea
Lehmannia marginata
Limax maximus
Monacha cantiana
Oxychilus alliarius
Oxychilus cellarius
Oxychilus helveticus
Punctum pygmaeum
Retinella nitidula
Tadonia budapestensis
Testacella haliotidea
Testacella scutulum
Trichia plebeia
Trichia striolata
Vitrea crystallina
Vitrina pellucida

CRUSTACEA : ISOPODA
Armadillidium vulgare
Haplophthalmus danicus
Oniscus asellus
Philoscia muscorum
Porcellio scaber
Trichoniscus pusillus

CHILOPODA
Lithobius calcaratus
Lithobius forficatus
Lithobius melanops
Necrophloeophagus flavus
Strigamia acuminata

DIPLOPODA
Brachydesmus superus
Cylindroiulus parisiorum
Cylindroiulus punctatus
Glomeris marginata
Julus scandinavius
Tachypodoiulus niger

GALL-CAUSING ORGANISMS
ACARI : Eriophyiidae
Eriophyes brevitarsus
Eriophyes filiformis
Eriophyes fraxinivora
Eriophyes laevis
Eriophyes leiosoma
Eriophyes macrochelus
Eriophyes macrorhynchus
Eriophyes megalonyx
Eriophyes tiliae
Eriophyes tristriatus
Eriophyes ulmi

HEMIPTERA : Psyllidae
Psylla buxi

DIPTERA : Cecidomyiidae
Contarinia tiliarum
Cystiphora sonchi
Dasineura crataegi
Dasineura urticae
Hartigiola annulipes
Rhopalomyia millefolii
Rondaniola bursaria
Taxomyia taxi

DIPTERA : Tephritidae
Urophora cardui

HYMENOPTERA : Cynipidae
Andricus anthracina
Andricus fecundator
Andricus lignicola
Andricus quercuscalicis
Biorrhiza pallida
Diplolepis rosae
Neuroterus albipes
Neuroterus numismalis
Neuroterus quercusbaccarum

HYMENOPTERA : Tenthredinidae
Pontania proxima

ORTHOPTERA
Chorthippus brunneus
Chorthippus parallelus
Leptophyes punctatissima
Meconema thalassinum
Metrioptera roeselii
Pholidoptera griseoaptera
Tetrix subulata
Tetrix undulata

HEMIPTERA
Acanthosoma haemorrhoidale
Capsus ater
Cercopis vulnerata
Cicadella viridis
Cixius nervosus
Coreus marginatus
Dryophilocoris flavoquadrimaculatus
Elasmostethus interstinctus
Elasmucha grisea
Euscelis incisus
Graphocephala fennahi
Heterogaster urticae
Ischnodemus sabuleti
Issus coleoptratus
Javesella dubia
Lygocoris viridis
Lygus rugulipennis
Nabis ferus
Palomena prasina
Picromerus bidens
Psallus diminutus
Scolopostethus thomsoni
Tingis ampliata
Troilus luridus

LEPIDOPTERA (Butterflies)

Thymelicus sylvestris	Small Skipper
Thymelicus lineola	Essex Skipper
Ochlodes venata	Large Skipper
Gonepteryx rhamni	Brimstone
Pieris brassicae	Large White
Pieris rapae	Small White
Pieris napi	Green-veined White
Anthocharis cardamines	Orange Tip
Quercusia quercus	Purple Hairstreak
Strymonidia w-album	White-letter Hairstreak
Lycaena phlaeas	Small Copper
Polyommatus icarus	Common Blue
Celastrina argiolus	Holly Blue
Vanessa atalanta	Red Admiral
Cynthia cardui	Painted Lady
Aglais urticae	Small Tortoiseshell
Inachis io	Peacock
Polygonia c-album	Comma
Pararge aegeria	Speckled Wood
Pyronia tithonus	Gatekeeper
Maniola jurtina	Meadow Brown
Coenonympha pamphilus	Small Heath
Aphantopus hyperantus	Ringlet

Freshwater Life

Recorders: M.W.Hanson, G.Wilkinson, S.Wilkinson, Pam Wilson, Peter Wilson, Sheila McDonald, Dr Peter Hammond, the late Stan Hudgell, Derek Smith

Records: 2000 - 2003

Hylands has a good range of freshwater habitat – with at least fifteen ponds of varying size, an ornamental serpentine lake – almost certainly the work of Humphry Repton – three areas of flowing water (River Wid, Sandy Brook and the culvert), a Ha-Ha ditch, a "moat" (at least a deliberately excavated linear/curved feature), a watercress bed (spring-fed) and "sedge-fens" – areas of very wet ground colonised by the sedge *Carex pendula*. Many of the ponds contain Great Crested Newts.

Not all the water bodies are permanent (ie the Ephemeral Pond), some at least partially dry-out in summer. Even so, the tiny Ephemeral Pond is probably the oldest in the park and has a unique flora and fauna (including Fine-leaved Water-dropwort and the damselfly *Lestes dryas*) and really merits further investigation and special conservation measures. The flowing water habitat obviously has its own specially adapted species; the culvert and Sandy Brook probably suffer from some polluted run-off from adjacent agricultural land. The River Wid, running extensively through agricultural land, is also vulnerable to pesticide and fertiliser run-off, but still provides for Water Vole, Otter, the damselfly *Platycnemis pennipes* and the local (RDB 3) Bryozoan *Lophopis crystallina*, which was recorded (as statoblasts in flood debris) from here in 2002. The Ha-Ha ditch south of the house is notably the home of the rare land leech *Trocheta subviridis*.

HYDROZOA
Hydra viridissima
Hydra vulgaris

TRICLADIDA
Dendrocoelum lacteum
Dugesia lugubris

BRYOZOA
Lophopis crystallina

MOLLUSCA
Acroloxus lacustris
Ancylus fluviatilis
Anodonta anatina
Anodonta cygnaea
Gyraulus albus
Gyraulus crista
Hippeutis complanatus
Lymnaea palustris
Lymnaea peregra
Lymnaea stagnalis
Musculium lacustre

MOLLUSCA cont.
Physa acuta
Pisidium personatum
Planorbarius corneus
Potamopyrgus antipodarum

HIRUDINEA
Glossiphonia complanata
Glossiphonia heteroclita
Helobdella stagnalis
Theromyzon tessulatum
Trocheta subviridis

MALACOSTRACA
Asellus aquaticus
Asellus meridianus
Crangonyx pseudogracilis
Gammarus pulex

EPHEMEROPTERA
Baetis vernus
Cloeon dipterum

ODONATA
Aeshna cyanea
Aeshna grandis
Aeshna mixta
Anax imperator
Calopteryx splendens
Coenagrion puella
Enallagma cyathigerum
Erythromma najas
Ischnura elegans
Lestes dryas
Lestes sponsa
Libellula depressa
Libellula quadrimaculata*
Orthetrum cancellatum
Platycnemis pennipes
Pyrrhosoma nymphula
Sympetrum sanguineum
Sympetrum striolatum

(*Recorded from Marconi Lake only)

HEMIPTERA
Gerris lacustris
Hesperocorixa sahlbergi
Microvelia reticulata
Nepa cinerea
Notonecta glauca
Rhopalosiphum nympheae
Sigara dorsalis
Velia caprai

COLEOPTERA
Agabus bipustulatus
Cercyon convexiusculus
Cercyon haemorrhoidalis
Cercyon impressus
Cercyon lateralis
Cercyon melanocephalus
Cercyon sternalis
Cryptopleurum minutum
Dytiscus sp.
Haliplus ruficollis
Helophorus aequalis
Helophorus brevipalpis
Helophorus obscurus
Hydrobius fuscipes
Hydroporus palustris
Hydroporus planus

COLEOPTERA cont.
Hygrotus inaequalis
Hyphydrus ovatus
Megasternum obscurum
Octhebius minimus
Suphrodytes dorsalis

MEGALOPTERA
Sialis lutaria

TRICHOPTERA
Hydropsyche pellucida
Mystacides azurea
Phryganea bipunctata

DIPTERA
Ablabesmyia monilis
Culiseta annulata
Ditichophora calceata
Hilara anglodanica
Hilara lurida
Hilara thoracica
Hydrodromia stagnalis
Hydromya dorsalis
Limnia unguicornis
Notiphila maculata
Parhelophilus frutetorum
Poecilobothrus nobilitatus
Raphium appendiculatum
Syntormon denticulatus
Syntormon pallipes
Tetanocera hyalipennis

PISCES
Carassius auratus (Goldfish)
Cyprinus carpio (Carp)
   (Mirror, Common and Koi)
Gasterosteus aculeatus (Stickleback)
Gobio gobio (Gudgeon)
Phoxinus phoxinus (Minnow)
Scardinius erythropthalmus (Rudd)

AMPHIBIA
Bufo bufo (Toad)
Rana temporaria (Frog)
Triturus cristatus (Great Crested Newt)
Triturus vulgaris (Common Newt)

MAMMALIA
Arvicola terrestris (Water Vole)
Lutra lutra (Otter)

AVES
Alcedo atthis (Kingfisher)
Anas platyrhynchos (Mallard)
Ardea cinerea (Heron)
Athya fuligula (Tufted Duck)
Branta canadensis (Canada Goose)
Fulica atra (Coot)
Gallinula chloropus (Moorhen)
Phalacrocorax carbo (Cormorant)
Tachybaptus ruficollis (Little Grebe)

HIGHER PLANTS
Alisma plantago-aquatica
Alnus glutinosa
Apium nodiflorum
Azolla filiculoides
Carex pseudocyperus
Ceratophyllum demersum
Ceratophyllum submersum
Chara globularis
Eleocharis palustris
Glyceria fluitans
Glyceria maxima
Iris pseudacorus
Lemna minor
Lemna minuta
Lycopus europaeus
Lythrum salicaria
Mentha aquatica
Nitella mucronata
Nuphar lutea
Nyhmphaea alba
Oenanthe aquatica
Osmunda regalis
Polygonum amphibium
Potamogeton crispus
Potamogeton natans
Ranunculus aquatilis
Ranunculus sceleratus
Sparganium erectum
Typha angustifolia
Typha latifolia
Veronica beccabunga
Veronia catenata

MOSS
Rhynchostegium riparioides

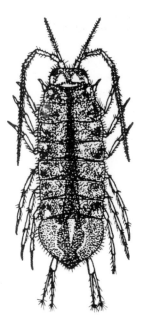

Asellus aquaticus

Hylands – Notable Species

Mark Hanson

Callicera spinolae **Rondani**   **Diptera : Syrphidae**

This species - the Golden Hoverfly, accorded Red Data Book 1 status - is the most significant invetebrate so far recorded at Hylands. I recorded a female at Ivy blossom in the formal gardens on the 21st of September 2001 and a male on the same patch of Ivy on the 24th September. Known as a British species only since 1928 when it was found at Southwold in Suffolk, it is entirely confined to East Anglia. Hylands is one of about four current sites known for this species (it may have disappeared from some former sites). It has recently been recorded from a site in Hertfordshire and another parkland site in Cambridgeshire - the National Trust's Wimpole Hall – where, like Hylands, it occurs with Callicera aurata, its close relative and other rare saproxylic hoverflies. From Wimpole Hall, Callicera spinolae was reared from a rot-hole in a Horse Chestnut tree, the tree species I suspect would be used at Hylands. The larva has, however, (in its European range) been recorded from rot-holes in various tree species, including Poplar, Ash, Field Maple and Beech. In Europe it is found in the Mediterranean area, France, Germany, Italy and Spain and is said to be a rare species throughout, indicating ancient forests of international importance.

Psilota anthracina **Meigen**   **Diptera : Syrphidae**

Another rare (RDB 2) saproxylic hoverfly. Unrecorded in Essex before the 1980s, it is an extremely elusive species. It often seems to be associated with old parks, but has also been found in Windsor and the New Forest. In Essex, true to form, it has turned-up only in Dagnam, Thorndon, Weald and Hylands Parks. The adults often visit Hawthorn flowers. I noted at least three, and probably a total of four, specimens on a flowering Cockspur Thorn (*Crataegus crus-galli*) in the formal gardens. At Hylands this particular thorn flowers slightly later than the Common Hawthorn. Little seems to be known of its life history, other than its larva has been recorded from accumulations of decaying wood and sap in rot-holes in trees.

Lestes dryas **(Kirby)**   **Odonata : Lestidae**

The once rare Scarce Emerald damselfly characteristic of coastal Essex had declined to such an extent by the 1970s that there were fears for its continued existence, not only in Essex, but also as a British breeding species. For several years, the species was barely recorded. However, by the mid-1980s some sort of recovery had been achieved and it was again recorded at a number of coastal sites in Essex. Typically it inhabits ditches and pools on the flood plains of rivers not far from the coast. I was quite surprised to capture and photograph a male of this species, as well as observing what was almost certainly a mating pair on the 14th July 2002 around the Ephemeral Pond in the southern part of Hylands. This pond also provided records of *Pyrrhosoma nymphula, Aeshna cyanea, Sympetrum sanguineum, Lestes sponsa* and *Ischnura elegans*. The pond dries out in the summer (not always fully), but still hosts an interesting flora, including Fine-leaved Water Dropwort (*Oenanthe aquatica*), Spike-rush (*Eleocharis palustris*) and Curled Pondweed (*Potamogeton crispus*). In Britain *Lestes dryas* is accorded RDB 2 status.

Trocheta subviridis **Dutrochet**   **Hirudinea : Erpobdellidae**

The spectacularly revolting Dutrochet's Land Leech is probably the largest invertebrate to occur in Hylands Park. Although difficult to measure, adults can be as much as 9ins (23cms) long when fully extended. At Hylands, it only seems to occur in the ha-ha ditch. Every year around about March time, the accumulations of fallen leaves from the previous autumn are removed revealing the presence of this species. It occurs between the irregular (sometimes broken) base of the ha-ha ditch and the bottom of the leaf pile and it seems to tolerate quite high levels of organic decay here. Over a period of three years I counted the numbers of leeches present and found the following:

2001	11	March 22nd
2002	16	April 11th (including 3 juveniles)
2003	63	March 26th (including 5 juveniles)

The 2003 count was possibly as a result of 'getting one's eye in', as they are not always easy to see in the decaying leaf debris at the bottom of the ditch. The leeches were carefully placed in or near water in the cleared areas and covered with wet leaves as we worked along the ditch; inevitably some must get discarded with the cleared leaves. Left visible they would be vulnerable to predation, but are fairly quickly able to insinuate themselves into the tiniest cracks in the ha-ha wall and base. The adults are known to be predators of earthworms and although not being fully equatic, will survive only in very wet ground and need to return to water to breed. Full breeding condition may be achieved after only three or four years.

Triturus cristatus **(Laurenti)**   **Amphibia : Salamandridae**

The famous Great Crested Newt is without doubt the commonest and most widely distributed amphibian at Hylands Park. By comparison, I have only ever seen one toad and three frogs at Hylands. In mainland Europe it appears to be a scarce species and the UK population is said to be amongst the largest. At Hylands it probably occurs in most of the ponds; as adults I have records from Ephemeral, Home Farm, Lake Field, Swan, Spring, Pigeon and Ice House ponds with records of their distinctive young from Ephemeral, Spring and Swan Ponds. It occurs occasionally in odd places; one I found under a wooden play-house near Flint Cottage, another I found about 3ft up in a decaying willow trunk by the Lake Field Pond. Strangely I have never seen it in either of the formal garden ponds, possibly because of the numbers of potential predators – ducks, moorhens and very large carp. The Great Crested Newt is protected by UK and European legislation.

Sesia apiformis **(Clerck)**   **Lepidoptera : Sesiidae**

Although not a rare moth, this species is notable because it is rarely seen and is a spectacular wasp mimic. The larvae feed in poplar wood for one or two years, before emerging as adults in late June and July. Grey Poplar seems to be a favourite host locally but other poplars are utilised. It seems to be at this moment in time a common species around Chelmsford. At Hylands, exit holes have been observed in hybrid poplar trees in the plantation nearly opposite the Lion Lawn. There have been reports of this species in the horticultural and national press being accorded pest status. It was implicated in the apparent death or dieback of poplars in Cambridgeshire, Bedfordshire and

Northamptonshire. Further research found that although the moth was present in many trees (particularly hybrid black poplars, *Populus* x *canadensis* var. *serotina*) it was also not present in many trees that were showing high levels of die-back. The moth larva when found in healthy trees seemed to have little deleterious effect, but when found in unhealthy or stressed trees, could contribute to their demise. Although not rare, the moth is still accorded nationally notable status.

Vespa crabro **Linnaeus**   **Hymenoptera : Vespidae**

The hornet is another species that is not uncommon nationally, but is notable at Hylands because it has been almost abundant in recent years. I have found very few nests, but those that I have found have been in hollow trees, under a large log (nest at ground level) and once in the roof space of a building. The queens were often found within the stable-block at Hylands, presumably looking for hibernation sites. The workers, males and the occasional queen, are attracted by Ivy blossom in the autumn and can be seen hunting other insects, notably hoverflies.

Testacella scutulum **Sowerby**   **Mollusca : Testacellidae**

This shelled slug and its close relative *Testacella haliotidea* Draparnaud, have both been recorded from flower beds in the formal gardens area. Despite being two apparently distinctive species, there is a possibility that they are one and the same, which should have the specific name *haliotidea*. Both species I dug-up from richly organic soil in the formal gardens, one of which I found appeared to be sucking an earthworm dry (both predate earthworms). The formal gardens would appear to be classic habitat for these invertebrates. Many 19th century records were from the kitchen gardens of country houses. There is a possibility that both species were introduced from the Mediterranean. Although very distinctive, with their tiny shells, neither species are often recorded and both are extremely rare in Essex.

Muscardinus avellanarius **(Linnaeus)**   **Rodentia : Gliridae**

For me the discovery of the dormouse at Hylands was second only to the discovery of *Callicera spinolae*. This attractive and much-loved resident of Britain's ancient countryside is thought to be a scarce and declining species. Its decline is thought to be through the loss and lack of management of its traditional habitat – ancient woodland. In Britain it now has a very southern distribution and Suffolk is about as far north as it gets. The species is, however, elusive and the Essex and Suffolk Dormouse project – through its nest-box scheme – is gaining more and more records of its present whereabouts and preferred habitat, which obviously includes mature scrub and overgrown hedgerows. It is thought that regular roadside hedge-flailing may not help this species because it prevents berries and fruits forming.

Because of the quality, diversity and extent of potential habitat at Hylands, I suspect a strong population of this animal is probably present. In the late summer of 2002, 26 nest-boxes were placed in the park and on later inspection two were found to be occupied with dormouse nests. The nests were of loosely woven grass with some dry leaves incorporated. A probable third nest was also discovered in the Lower Belt area.

Lutra lutra (Linnaeus)   **Carnivora : Mustelidae**

This is very probably the most surprising and startling record from Hylands Park. Otters, although apparently common in the 19th century Essex, suffered a catastrophic decline in the late 20th century and may have actually become extinct in the county. The possibility that this may be the situation throughout East Anglia, prompted the Otter Trust - based in Suffolk - to initiate a breeding and release programme.

The University of Essex supported a new otter research programme in 1996 and by 1997, had recorded otter on the River Wid near Writtle. Subsequently, evidence of otter – usually in the form of spraints – has been recorded on the Wid in Hylands Park in the years 1998 – 2003, although this is unfortunately not evidence for a re-established breeding holt. It would be possible, giving continued lack of disturbance along the Wid, pro-otter bankside management and planting and even the construction of an artificial holt to enhance the habitat and possibly encourage the otter to breed.

Hericium cirrhatum (Pers. : Fr.) Karst.   **Fungi : Hericiaceae**

This rare fungus was found in January 2001 in the eastern part of the park near the large Walnut (*Juglans regia*) actually on decaying log-wood from another felled Walnut. In Essex, outside Epping Forest, this species (and other *Hericium* spp.) are virtually unknown. Nationally it is also considered to be a rare species.

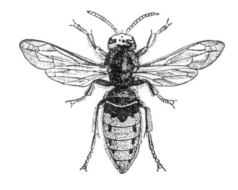

Vespa crabro

The Higher Plants of Hylands Park

Recorders : K.J.Adams, Alec Bull, M.W.Hanson, the late Stan Hudgell, Tim Pyner, G.Smith, G.Wilkinson, S.Wilkinson

Records : 2000 – 2003

Because of the diversity of habitat at Hylands, including ancient woodland, old grasslands and still and running fresh water, a remarkable 436 species of vascular plant were recorded here between 2000 and 2003. I do not have full lists from other Essex parks for comparison, but the list for Moccas Park, Herefordshire (a national nature reserve) which is a much smaller, earlier and heavily grazed park, has only 259 recorded species. I suspect that the current limited grazing by deer and no domestic livestock has at least made it easier to record plants at Hylands, although some of the mown grasslands, particularly those surrounding the formal gardens area, I suspect are fairly species-rich, but difficult to survey because of the constant mowing.

Despite the good number of plant taxa recorded, no spectacular rarities have turned-up. I suspect that this is, in part, due to much of the park being created out of an ordinary 18th century farmed landscape. The majority of the plants we see today are direct descendants of those that occurred here in the Georgian period.

It is not possible to provide an annotated checklist of all the taxa recorded for reasons of space. The check-lists below are selected from the more interesting, notable or indicator species (but include some of the more mundane as well!). They are listed by habitat.

Ancient Woodland

The principal ancient woodland area is South Wood, covering approximately 30 acres. It sits, at least in part, on chalky boulder clay which gives a calcareous feel to the flora. It is a coppice with standards. The standard trees include Oak, Ash, Hornbeam and Field Maple, the coppice stools, Hornbeam, Ash and Elm. There are very old Elm stools on the western edge of the wood and ancient ash in the south-eastern sector. There is noticeable sycamore invasion in places. Smaller areas of ancient woodland include Writtle Wood, Lightfoot Spring, the Tower and Lower Belts and a small part of the formal gardens. Wild Service tree is characteristic of some of these locations.

Trees and Shrubs recorded from ancient woodland

Acer campestre	*Crataegus monogyna*	*Quercus robur*
Carpinus betulus	*Euonymus europaeus*	*Sorbus torminalis*
Cornus sanguinea	*Fraxinus excelsior*	*Taxus baccata*
Corylus avellana	*Ilex aquifolium*	*Ulmus glabra*
Crataegus laevigata	*Malus sylvestris*	*Viburnum opulus*

Herbaceous Plants recorded from ancient woodland

Allium ursinum	*Epipactis purpurata*	*Milium effusum*
Arum maculatum	*Geum urbanum*	*Moerhingia trinervia*
Brachypodium sylvaticum	*Hyacynthoides non-scripta*	*Orchis mascula*
Bromopsis ramosus	*Iris foetidissima*	*Polystichum aculeatum*
Carex pendula	*Listera ovata*	*Polystichum setiferum*
Carex sylvatica	*Lonicera periclymenum*	*Primula vulgaris*
Daphne laureola	*Lysimachia nummularia*	*Ranunculus auricomus*
Dryopteris carthusiana	*Melica uniflora*	*Veronica montana*
Dryopteris filix mas	*Mercurialis perennis*	*Viola reichenbachiana*

Grassland

Hylands has a good range of grassland types, from long established old to newly created. As a rule of thumb, the oldest grasslands are in the southern sector of the park; the new are in the north. The latter are sown grass, created from former arable fields re-incorporated into the park and now managed as hay meadow. Geologically the park is London Clay overlain by chalky boulder clay and head (possibly with very minor superficial deposits of pebbly gravel and sand). All these occur at the surface and there is a correspondingly diverse mosaic of probably unclassifiable grassland within the park boundary running from acid to calcareous.

Acid (Formal Gardens)

Calluna vulgaris	*Hypericum humifusum*
Carex ovalis	*Potentilla erecta*
Galium saxatile	*Rumex acetosella*

Calcareous (Writtle Hills)*

Briza media	*Trifolium ochroleucon*
Hordeum secalinum	*Trisetum flavescens*
Primula veris	

Because of their diverse nature and extent, I suspect that the grasslands at Hylands constitute one of the most important assemblages remaining in Essex. It is probable that Essex has lost some 98% of its old flower-rich meadows to agricultural intensification.

*This tiny patch of very old grassland has over forty species of higher plant in it. Others include *Dactylorhiza fuchsii, Conopodium majus* and *Juncus articulatus*.

Over 120 species of grassland-dependent plants have been recorded at Hylands. An extensive (but not complete) list is given here (listed by family). It includes species from new as well as old grassland and also species from dry and wet, as well as those found in developing scrub.

Ranunculaceae

Ranunculus acris
Ranunculus bulbosus
Ranunculus repens

Cruciferae

Cardamine pratensis

Hypericaceae

Hypericum hirsutum
Hypericum perforatum

Caryophyllaceae

Cerastium fontanum
Stellaria graminea
Stellaria holostea

Leguminosae

Lathyrus nissolia
Lathyrus pratensis
Lotus corniculatus
Lotus uliginosus
Medicago arabica
Medicago lupulina
Ononis repens
Trifolium dubium
Trifolium hybridum
Trifolium pratense
Trifolium repens
Vicia cracca
Vicia hirsuta
Vicia sativa
Vicia sepium
Vicia tetrasperma

Rosaceae

Agrimonia eupatoria
Filipendula ulmaria
Fragaria vesca
Potentilla anserina
Potentilla erecta
Potentilla sterilis
Rosa arvensis
Rosa canina
Rosa rubiginosa
Rosa stylosa
Rosa tomentosa

Umbelliferae

Anthriscus sylvestris
Conopodium majus
Heracleum sphondylium
Pastinaca sativa
Torilis japonica

Polygonaceae

Rumex acetosa
Rumex acetosella
Rumex crispus
Rumex obtusifolius

Gentianaceae

Centaurium erythraea

Scrophulariaceae

Veronica chamaedrys
Veronica filiformis

Lamiacae

Clinopodium vulgare
Prunella vulgaris
Stachys officinalis

Plantaginaceae

Plantago lanceolatus
Plantago major

Rubiaceae

Galium mollugo
Galium verum

Dipsacaceae

Dipsacus fullonum
Knautia arvensis

Compositae

Achillea millefolium
Bellis perennis
Centaurea nigra
Cirsium arvense
Cirsium palustre
Crepis capillaris
Crepis vesicaria
Hieracium pilosella
Hypochoeris radicata
Leontodon autumnalis
Leontodon hispidus
Leucanthemum vulgare
Pulicaria dysenterica
Senecio erucifolius
Senecio jacobaea

Juncaceae

Juncus articulatus
Juncus effusus
Juncus inflexus

Orchidaceae

Dactylorhiza fuchsii
Ophrys apifera

Cyperaceae

Carex divulsa
Carex flacca
Carex hirta
Carex nigra
Carex otrubae
Carex pallescens
Carex spicata
Isolepis setacea

Gramineae

Agrostis capillaris
Agrostis stolonifera
Alopecurus pratensis
Anthoxanthum odoratum
Arrhenatherum elatius
Bromus hordeaceus
Cynosurus cristatus
Dactylis glomerata
Deschampsia caespitosa
Elytrygia repens
Festuca arundinacea
Festuca pratensis
Festuca rubra
Holcus lanatus
Holcus mollis
Hordeum secalinum
Lolium perenne
Phleum bertolonii
Phleum pratense
Poa annua
Poa pratensis
Poa trivialis
Trisetum flavescens

Some Noteworthy Plants

Chara globularis Recorded from the Swan Pond in July 2002.

Osmunda regalis (**Royal Fern**) Originally six clumps of this fern grew in the formal gardens lake – of these, five are now dead and the sixth is producing very few fronds. A single small plant was noted on the bank of the Serpentine Lake.

Polypodium **sp. (Polypody)** Three small immature plants of polypody were found growing on a nearly prostrate living hawthorn trunk in dense scrub just east of South Wood in 2001. By December 2002, they had still not produced sori and hence it has not been possible to determine the species.

Polystichum setiferum (**Soft Shield Fern**) Found in South Wood in small numbers in 2002.

Polystichum aculeatum (**Hard Shield Fern**) A single plant found in March 2003 in the Lower Belt. There is a c.1980 record for South Wood.

Ranunculus sardous (**Hairy Buttercup**) This bizarre record is from Ventrises Field, one of the 'new' hay meadows in the north part of the park. Usually a species of estuarine grazing marsh, it turned-up with *Trifolium resupinatum* (Reversed Clover) by a track way across the field in 2001 and 2002.

Montia fontana (**Blinks**) Uncommon in Essex, but found in three places in the formal gardens area in 2002 - mainly in imported gravel on a path, but also in areas of lawn.

Ononis repens (**Common Rest harrow**) Typically a plant of the chalky boulder clay, this species occurs on the London Road verge at its southern-most end, in some quantity, recorded 2001 and 2002.

Sorbus torminalis (**Wild Service**) Mature but small trees have been found in South Wood, Tower Belt, Lower Belt and Lightfoot Spring. It is classically a species of ancient woodland often found on boundary banks.

Daphne laureola (**Spurge Laurel**) Another plant of the till, this species occurs in some quantity in the Tower Belt, South Wood and Pigeon Plantation.

Viscum album (**Mistletoe**) Most frequent on Lime (*Tilia* x *vulgaris*) at Hylands, one tree of which is more like a mistletoe tree. Other trees parasitised include Hawthorn, Hybrid Poplar, Birch and Red Horse Chestnut.

Conopodium majus (**Pignut**) Surprisingly widespread at Hylands, mainly in grass, but occasionally in woodland. It is frequent on the north-western margin of the Lake Field and by the main gate car park. An indicator species for old grassland.

Silaum silaus (**Pepper Saxifrage**) Much declined in Essex with the destruction of its old grassland habitat. At Hylands I have only ever found a single plant in the Ha-Ha ditch.

Calluna vulgaris (**Heather**) Noted as three tiny plants in the acid grassland area in the formal gardens in 2001 and flowering once protected from mowing in 2002. This species, with others such as *Galium saxatile* (Heath Bedstraw), *Carex ovalis* (Oval Sedge), the moss *Polytrichum juniperinum* and the wasp *Astata boops*, may indicate a tiny fragment of relict heathland (rather like Galleywood Common).

Primula veris **(Cowslip)** Another much declined plant of chalk grassland in Essex. The colony on Writtle Hills, maintained by giving the grass a late cut, consisted of just over a hundred plants in 2002.

Stachys officinalis **(Betony)** Another old grassland plant losing ground in Essex. A large patch of this plant is found in the species-rich grassland east of South Wood.

Allium ursinum **(Wild Garlic, Ramsons)** Usually found in ancient woodland, this lovely spring-flowering plant with its strongly garlic-smelling leaves is found in Lightfoot Spring and oddly by the pergola in the formal gardens.

Epipactis purpurata **(Violet Helleborine)** The only species listed not found 2000 – 2003, the species was recorded in the late 1990s from South Wood and the Lower Belt. Like *Listera ovata* (Common Twayblade), also found in South Wood (about 30 spikes in 2002), it is probably eaten by deer.

Ophrys apifera **(Bee Orchid)** Relatively common in Essex, I have found this species at six locations at Hylands. Most are in the southern park, present in 2001 and 2002.

Orchis mascula **(Early Purple Orchid)** The most abundant orchid at Hylands and one of the sensational botanical sights. There are probably over 500 plants (but not all will be in flower) in part of South Wood. The colour is quite variable – mostly around purple, but a few had pinky-white flowers in 2002.

Carex pallescens **(Pale Sedge)** Very rare in Essex, I found a couple of plants near South Wood, not far from the Betony colony in July 2002.

Carex pseudocyperus **(Cyperus sedge)** This attractive aquatic sedge is now uncommon in Essex. At Hylands it is well known from the Ice-House Pond, but has also recently turned-up at the Spring Pond.

Isolepis setacea **(Bristle Scirpus)** This rare Essex plant turned-up in quantity on the north lawn in 2001 – possibly over an area of 1,000 square feet. It is normally a plant of patches of bare ground poached by livestock.

Briza media **(Quaking Grass)** Another scarce old grassland species it is, however, not uncommon in the south-west grasslands at Hylands.

Note: A list of higher plants found in fresh water habitats is contained in the section on fresh water life p.127.

A list of plants from disturbed grounds is to be found in the section on pests and pathogens p.160.

Plants not yet recorded at Hylands:

Lamiastrum galaeobdolon (Yellow Archangel)

Ophioglossum vulgatum (Adders-tongue)

Anacamptis pyramidalis (Pyramidal Orchid)

Pimpinella saxifraga (Burnet Saxifrage)

Ruscus aculeatus (Butchers Broom)

Hylands Park: miscellaneous trees

1. *Castanea sativa* 2. *Crataegus monogyna*   4. *Acer platanoides* 5. *Taxus baccata*
3. *Crataegus laevigata*

6. *Cercis siliquastrum* 7. *Fagus sylvatica* 8. *Carpinus betulus*

9. *Sorbus torminalis* 10. *Sorbus intermedia* 11. *Sorbus aria*

12. *Tilia cordata* 13. *Alnus glutinosa* 14. *Alnus incana* 15. *Populus tremulus*

Special Studies

The Elms (*Ulmus* spp. and hybrids)

Hylands has a good list of elm taxa. It would probably be one of the best sites to undertake a DNA-based study of elms, because of this diversity within a relatively small area. Despite the presence of Dutch Elm Disease since the 1970s (and still active in the park) there are quite a number of mature 'identifiable' elms, although none of these are sizeable specimens. Much of this diversity, I suspect, is through deliberate planting rather than natural occurrence. Obvious plantings are the avenue that existed near the Margaretting Gate – the suckers of the English Elms that grew here still survive in two straight lines either side of what was, at one time, a public road. English Elm was a fashionable planted tree of the first half of the 19th century. Other plantings must include the Dutch Elm in Ice-House plantation and the probable Huntingdon Elm in the formal gardens (a fashion tree of 1890 – 1920). Other elms must be of planted origin in the Home Farm, Swan Pond and River Wid plantations and also the formal gardens area. Native elms – notably Wych Elm – occur in South Wood. There are a number of obviously very old Wych Elm stools here. A probable Wych/East Anglian hybrid occurs in the Green Lane. Wych elm also occurs as presumably a planted tree in the formal gardens. The accompanying leaf silhouettes indicate the location of some of the park's elms.

Elms Recorded at Hylands

Wych Elm (*Ulmus glabra*)

English Elm (*Ulmus procera*)

East Anglian Elm (*Ulmus minor* 'sensu lato' in a least three forms)

Hybrid Elms: *Ulmus* x *hollandica* (Dutch Elm)
                 Ulmus x *vegeta* (Huntingdon Elm)?
                 Ulmus glabra x *minor* (naturally occurring)

Recent Elm: *Ulmus* 'Sapporo Autumn Gold'

Ulmus 'Sapporo Autumn Gold' occurs as two trees in the arboretum, planted at the north margin of Writtle Hills. The tree is thought to be a hybrid between *Ulmus pumila* and *Ulmus japonica*. The trees were supplied by Pitney Bowes of Harlow as part of their 'Elms across Europe' campaign of the 1980s, to replace elms killed by Dutch Elm Disease with a disease-resistant tree.

Hylands Park: Elm (*Ulmus*)

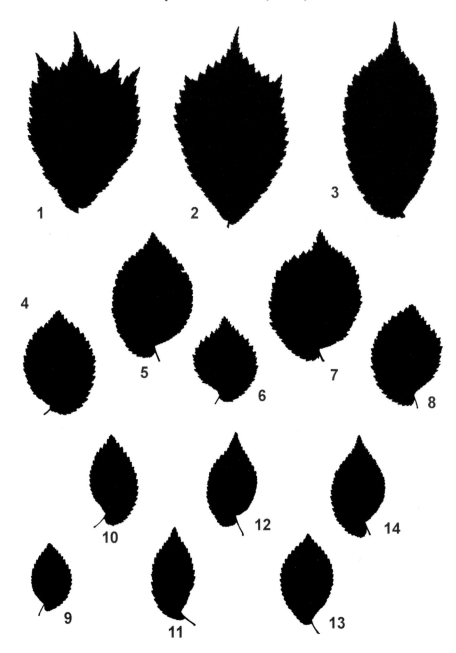

Ulmus glabra
1. London Rd. (nr. R. Wid)
2. Home Farm
3. Formal Gardens

Ulmus procera
4. Green Lane
5. Formal Gardens
6. London Rd. (N.)
7. Writtle by-pass
8. Nr. Main Gate

Ulmus minor
9. Nr. Main Gate
10. Home Farm
11. London Rd. (nr. R. Wid)
12. Swan Pond Plnt.
13. Formal Gardens
14. Writtle by-pass

Hylands Park: Hybrid Elms (*Ulmus* x)

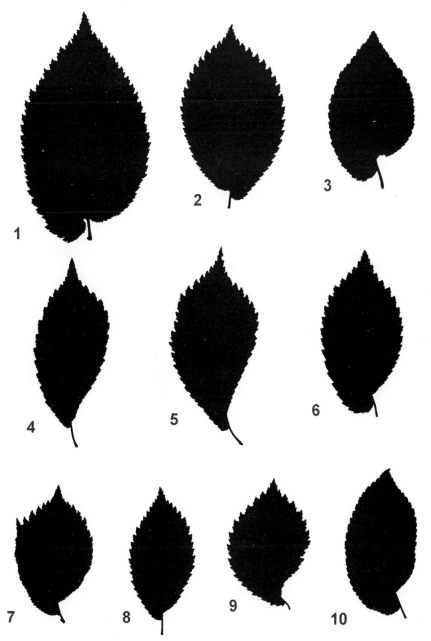

1. *Ulmus* x *hollandica* (Dutch Elm) Ice House Plnt.
2. *Ulmus* x *vegeta* (Hunt. Elm) Formal Gdns.
3. *Ulmus* x ? (leaf resembles *U. coritana*) R. Wid Plnt.
4-10. Miscellaneous putative hybrids?
    Most probably *minor* x *glabra*

4. Formal Gdns.
5. Flint Cottage
6. Oak Plnt.
7. Swan Pond
8. Green Lane
9. London Rd. (nr. Widford Bridge)
10. Home Farm

The Brambles (*Rubus fruticosus* agg.)

Alec Bull, the Norfolk Rubus specialist, visited Hylands on July 2nd 2002. Brambles (Blackberries) are common throughout Essex. In most species lists they are 'lumped' together under the all-embracing '*Rubus fruticosus* agg.'. In fact, there are probably many hundreds of species in Britain – some widespread and common, others local to the point of being found only at one site and many are un-named. Because of the difficulties with naming blackberries, identification is a job for the specialist batologist and this is the reason why very few sites in Essex have reliable, accurately identified lists of brambles. Amongst those to have been investigated are Epping Forest, Danbury Common and Galleywood Common.

Epping Forest has 39 identified species recorded. Danbury Common has over 35 species. Hylands is the first time in Essex a comprehensive list has been obtained form a park. Parks are not always good for brambles – deer (both fallow and especially Muntjac in recent times) are very fond of blackberry leaves. Alan Newton (the national expert) once visited Windsor Great Park with a view to looking at its Rubi but on inspection, there apparently weren't any - the deer had eaten them all! Hylands is different – it never was a medieval deer park and has probably never had the intense grazing pressure that deer parks can be subject to. The landscape has also only relatively recently become a park. The brambles are probably more typical of an average 18th century farmed Essex landscape.

At Hylands, Alec Bull and I visited what I considered would be the most productive bramble sites - South Wood and its vicinity, the formal gardens, Roman Walk, Oak Plantation and the eastern boundary wall. Surprisingly a total of only eleven species (excepting introductions) were recorded:

Rubus amplificatus	*Rubus hindii*	*Rubus ulmifolius*
Rubus armipotens	*Rubus insectifolius*	*Rubus vestitus*
Rubus britannicus	*Rubus rufescens*	*Rubus wirralensis*
Rubus dasyphyllus	*Rubus tuberculatus*	

Most of the species are known to be widespread in the U.K. However, *R. armipotens* is mainly a south-eastern species. *R. britannicus* is mainly southern, whilst *R. tuberculatus* tends to be western in distribution. *Rubus ulmifolius* and *R. vestitus* are said to be the commonest brambles in Essex, followed by *R. rufescens*. *Rubus ulmifolius* x *vestitus* was also recorded and is said to be the commonest sterile hybrid in the U.K.

In addition to these species, four introduced Rubi are known from Hylands:

Rubus armeniacus – the so-called Himalayan Giant, notably found in the formal gardens and the walled kitchen garden, is presumably a relict from the days when Hylands had working kitchen gardens. Raspberry (*Rubus idaeus*) was also found near the London Road boundary wall, another escape from cultivation. The beautiful deciduous hybrid *Rubus* 'Benenden' and the ground-covering *Rubus tricolor*, originally from China, can both be found in the formal gardens area.

References

Bull, A. (1996) The Bramble Flora of Epping Forest
    Essex Naturalist (New Series) Vol. 13 pp.116 – 120

Hanson, M.W. (1990) Essex Elm. *Essex Naturalist* (New Series) No. 10 pp.1 – 88

Jermyn, S.T. (1974) *The Flora of Essex*. Essex Naturalists' Trust

Bryophytes from Hylands Park

Recorder : Tim Pyner

Records   :   2002 – 2003

Mosses

Amblystegium serpens	Hennediella macrophylla	
Atrichum undulatum	Homalia trichomanoides	
Aulacomnium androgynum	Homalothecium sericeum	
Barbula unguiculata	Hypnum cupressiforme	
Brachythecium albicans	Hypnum jutlandicum	
Brachythecium rutabulum	Hypnum resupinatum	
Brachythecium velutinum	Isothecium myosuroides	
Bryum argenteum	Leptobryum pyriforme	
Bryum bicolour	Leptodictyum riparium	
Bryum caespiticium	Mnium hornum	
Bryum capillare	Orthodontium lineare	
Bryum rubens	Orthotrichum affine	
Bryum subelegans	Orthotrichum anomalum	
Calliergonella cuspidata	Orthotrichum diaphanum	
Campylopus introflexus	Orthotrichum lyellii	
Ceratodon purpureus	Orthotrichum stramineum	
Cratoneuron filicinum	Plagiomnium undulatum	
Cryphaea heteromalla	Plagiothecium curvifollium	
Dicranella heteromalla	Plagiothecium succulentum	
Dicranoweisia cirrata	Polytrichum formosum	
Dicranum tauricum	Polytrichum juniperinum	
Ditrichum cylindricum	Pseudocrossidium hornschuchianum	
Didymodon insulanus	Rhizomnium punctatum	
Didymodon luridus	Rhynchostegium confertum	
Didymodon sinuosus	Rhynchostegium riparioides	
Didymodon tophaceus	Rhytidiadelphus squarrosus	
Didymodon vinealis	Schistidium crassipilum	
Ephemerum serratum	Syntrichia intermedia	
Eurhynchium hians	Syntrichia latifolia	
Eurhynchium praelongum	Thamnobryum alopecurum	
Eurhynchium pumilum	Tortula acaulon	
Fissidens bryoides	Tortula marginata	
Fissidens exilis	Tortula muralis	
Fissidens incurvus	Tortula truncata	
Fissidens taxifolius	Ulota bruchii	
Funaria hygrometrica	Ulota crispa	
Grimmia pulvinata	Ulota phyllantha	
Gyroweisia tenuis	Zygodon viridissimus	

Liverworts

Frullania dilatata
Lophocolea bidentata
Lophocolea heterophylla
Lunularia cruciata
Metzgeria fruticulosa
Metzgeria furcata
Pellia endiviifolia

Lichens of Hylands Park

John Skinner

Recorders : John Skinner and Tim Pyner

Records : 2000 – 2002

Nomenclature follows 'The Lichen Flora of Great Britain and Ireland' by Purvis et al (1992) with a few recent changes.

The principal habitats of interest, from the point of view of their lichen flora, are:

The perimeter wall of the Park

The part examined was in the north east sector, beside the A414 (London Road), but all remaining sections of old brick wall are potentially of interest. The lichen flora is typical of established brickwork with *Lecanora atra* and *Buellia* and *Trapelia* species.

Low garden walls near the House

Low flagstone-capped walls bear an interesting flora with *Sarcogyne simplex* and *Lecidella carpathica,* neither species particularly common in Essex, although easily overlooked.

Ash, Walnut and Willow trees

The most luxuriant lichen growth in the park is seen on sloping Ash and Willow trees, particularly near ponds. In this situation, trunks are covered with *Parmelia* species and the two similar species (split fairly recently) *Punctelia subrudecta* and *P. ulophylla*. On one Willow tree, *Candelariella reflexa* was found fertile, which is unusual. A large old Walnut tree near the House was also well covered with lichens, including *Parmelia saxatilis,* not yet found elsewhere in the park. The conspicuous species *Parmelia caperata* and *P. perlata,* which have both spread and increased rapidly in Essex over the last ten years, were both found several times.

Tree stumps

Tree stumps, particularly in the formal gardens, were well colonised by *Cladonia* species. Although no rare species were found, it emphasises the importance of rotten wood as a lichen substratum.

A total of 61 lichens were recorded, 33 associated in some way with trees and 28 with brick, mortar and imported flagstones.

Amandinea punctata	:	bark of Ash, Elder, Walnut, Willow
Acarospora fuscata	:	flagstones of garden wall
Anisomeridium nyssaegenum	:	Elder
Buellia aethalea	:	brick boundary wall
Buellia verruculosa	:	brick boundary wall
Caloplaca citrina	:	mortar of boundary wall
Caloplaca holocarpa	:	mortar of boundary wall
Candelariella aurella	:	bricks of boundary wall
Candelariella reflexa	:	bark of Willow (fertile)
Candelariella vitellina	:	brick boundary wall, flagstones of garden wall
Catillaria chalybeia	:	bricks of boundary wall
Cladonia chlorophaea	:	ground in garden
Cladonia coniocraea	:	tree stump in garden

Cladonia fimbriata	:	tree stump in garden
Cladonia macilenta	:	stump of Oak
Cladonia pyxidata	:	bricks of boundary wall
Dimerella diluta	:	shaded bark of Ash
Diploicia canescens	:	bark of Ash, Willow
Evernia prunastri	:	Azalea, Walnut, Willow
Hypogymnia physodes	:	Willow
Lecanora albescens	:	mortar of boundary wall
Lecanora atra	:	brick boundary wall
Lecanora campestris	:	mortar of boundary wall
Lecanora conizaeoides	:	bark of Ash, Plane, Willow, Sycamore brick boundary wall
Lecanora dispersa	:	mortar of boundary wall
Lecanora muralis	:	bricks of boundary wall, flagstones of garden wall
Lecanora polytropa	:	flagstones of garden wall
Lecidea fuscoatra	:	flagstones of garden wall
Lecidella carpathica	:	flagstones of garden wall
Lecidella scabra	:	bricks of boundary wall
Lecidella stigmatea	:	flagstones of garden wall
Lepraria incana	:	Azalea, Sycamore
Leproloma vouauxii	:	brick walls of Stable Block
Parmelia caperata	:	Azalea, Sycamore, Walnut, Willow
Parmelia perlata	:	Sycamore, Ash, Walnut
Parmelia revoluta	:	Sycamore
Parmelia saxatilis	:	Walnut
Parmelia subaurifera	:	bark of Sycamore, Walnut
Parmelia sulcata	:	bark of Ash, Plane, Walnut, Willow, Sycamore
Phaeophyscia orbicularis	:	bark of Sycamore, Willow; flagstones of garden wall
Phlyctis argena	:	Willow
Physcia adscendens	:	brick boundary wall, bark of Ash, Azalea, Willow
Physcia caesia	:	fallen Sycamore
Physcia tenella	:	Ash, Elder, Willow (all fertile), Walnut
Physcia grisea	:	fallen Sycamore
Platismatia glauca	:	Oak
Porpidia soredizodes	:	brick boundary wall
Psilolechia lucida	:	garden wall
Punctelia subrudecta	:	Ash, Walnut,
Punctelia ulophylla	:	Ash, Willow
Ramalina farinacea	:	bark of Ash, Walnut, Willow
Rhizocarpon obscuratum	:	coping of boundary wall
Sarcogyne simplex	:	flagstones of garden wall
Scoliciosporum chlorococcum	:	bark of Willow
Trapelia obtegens	:	bricks of boundary wall
Trapelia placodioides	:	eroding bricks, boundary wall, flagstones of garden wall
Trapeliopsis flexuosa	:	huge log by Drive
Xanthoria calcicola	:	brick buttress of boundary wall
Xanthoria parietina	:	bark of Ash, Azalea, Elder, Willow, Sycamore,
Xanthoria polycarpa	:	bark of Ash, Elder, Walnut, Willow,
Xanthoria ucrainica	:	bark of Sycamore

Fungi from Hylands Park

Tony Boniface

Recorders : Tony Boniface, Steven Wilkinson, M.W.Hanson

Records : 2000 - 2002

Hylands Park provides a variety of habitats for fungi ranging from ancient woodland, plantation, dead wood, rough grassland, mown lawns, and flower beds.

Bracket fungi on living and dead trees are well represented:-

Inonotus dryadeus Oak Bracket is found near the base of mature oaks often covered in golden drops.
Ganoderma resinaceum has a lacquered surface and greyish-white pores.
Ganoderma australe (=adspersum) Southern Bracket has a large perennial fruiting body.
Meripilus giganteus Giant Polypore has numerous fan-shaped outgrowths which slowly turn black when bruised.
Fistulina hepatica Poor Man's Beefsteak exudes a red liquid.
Polyporus squamosus Dryad's Saddle forms thin, large, scaly brackets early in the season.
Daedaleopsis confragosa Blushing Bracket has a pore surface which turns reddish when bruised.
Laetiporus sulphureus Chicken of the Woods has large orange-yellow fruiting bodies.
Piptoporus betulinus Birch Polypore has been used to strop razors and as tinder.
Trametes versicolor Turkey-tail Bracket has a multibanded upper surface.
Stereum hirsutum Hairy Crust has a smooth fertile surface without gills, tubes or teeth.
Auricularia auricula-judae Wood Ear is a gelatinous fungus usually found on elder.
Auricularia mesenterica Tripe Crust has a irregularly wrinkled lower surface.
Daedalea quercina Oak Maze-gill has maze-like pores on the under surface.
Inonotus hispidus Shaggy Bracket has a hairy to bristly upper surface.
Bjerkandera adusta Smoky Bracket has dark grey pores.
Pleurotus cornucopiae Branched Oyster has gills which branch and form a network over the top of the stem.
Chondrostereum purpureum Silver Leaf Fungus has a pink to violaceous colour.
Polyporus durus Bay Polypore has a white, cream or tan upper surface.
Polyporus leptocephalus Blackfoot Polypore has a dark brown to bay upper surface.
Hohenbuehelia geogenia has a tongue to funnel-shaped cap split down one side with decurrent gills down an excentric stem.
Pleurotus dryinus Veiled Oyster has a ring on the stem when young.

It is important to leave dead trunks and branches in situ to enable lignicolous species to establish themselves. Such species include:-

Pluteus cervinus Deer Shield has pink spores.
Xylaria hypoxylon Candle Snuff Fungus is very common.
Gymnopilus penetrans Common Rustgill has an orange brown cap and, sometimes a scented smell.
Gymnopilus junonius Juno's Rustgill is also known as the great big laughing Gymnopilus.
Exidia glandulosa Witches' Butter has jelly-like fruiting bodies.
Mycena inclinata Clustered Bonnet occurs in dense tufts.

Hypholoma fasciculare Sulphur Tuft is extremely common.

Tapinella (Paxillus) atrotomentosa Velvet Rollrim has a velvety fruiting body and grows on pine stumps. It is rare in Essex.

Gymnopus (=Collybia) fusipes Spindle Tough-shank grows in clumps at the base of deciduous trees.

Xylaria polymorpha Dead Man's Fingers is much larger than the Candle Snuff Fungus.

Daldinia concentrica King Alfred's Cakes grows mainly on ash.

Hypoxylon fragiforme Beech Woodwort is one of several species with black outgrowths on dead wood.

Coprinus micaceous Glistening Inkcap is the commonest ink cap and has mica-like flakes on the cap.

Resupinatus applicatus Smoked Oyster is a small fungus without a stalk with gills radiating from a central point.

Rhodotus palmatus Wrinkled Elm Cap is pink and is usually found on elm.

Xerula radicata Rooting Shank is a very tall fungus with a long root attached to tree roots especially beech.

Lycoperdon pyriforme Stump Puffball is the only puffball found on wood.

Crucibulum leave Common Bird's Nest is usually found on dead twigs and branches.

Kuehneromyces mutabilis has markedly hygrophanous caps found in clumps on stumps.

Ramaria stricta Upright Coral is a yellowish-brown coral fungus often found on buried tree roots.

Flammulina velutipes Velvet Shank has a dark brown velvety stalk.

Nectria cinnabarina is the Coral Spot Fungus.

Armillaria mellea Honey Fungus is a dangerous parasite of trees and shrubs.

Dacrymyces stillatus Orange Jelly has small, cushion-shaped, orange-yellow fruiting bodies.

Bulgaria inquinans Black Bulgar has black, rubbery fruiting bodies.

Bisporella citrina Lemon Elfcup has very small, saucer-shaped, yellow cups.

Phlebia radiata Wrinkled Crust grows flat on the bark of dead trees. It has a wrinkled, orange surface.

Tremella mesenterica Yellow Brain Fungus consists of gelatinous lobes and folds.

Coprinus atramentarius Common Inkcap is associated with buried wood. It causes very unpleasant symptoms when eaten with alcohol.

Coprinus disseminatus Fairy Inkcap occurs on or near tree stumps in extremely large groups.

Hericium cirrhatum Tiered Tooth is a Red Data List species which is recorded as vulnerable ie likely to become endangered. It was found on the end of a fallen walnut in January 2001. It has not been found since.

Psathyrella candolleana Pallid Fragicap grows in brittle clumps on or near dead wood.

Marasmiellus ramealis Twig Parachute is commonly found on bramble stems.

Several other gasteroid fungi which have spores developing in closed fruiting bodies have been recorded in the park:-

Scleroderma verrucosum Scaly Earthball.

Phallus impudicus Stinkhorn.

Calvatia gigantea Giant Puffball.

Lycoperdon perlatum Common Puffball.

Scleroderma areolatum Leopard Earthball.

Scleroderma citrinum Common Earthball.

The large trees in the park both in the woodland and grassland areas often grow in association with fungi forming mycorrhiza or fungus roots, which are a mutualistic relationship in which the fungal hyphae act as supplementary root hairs for the tree absorbing minerals and water from the soil. There are several genera which form mycorrhiza that occur in the park including the boletes that have tubes instead of gills under the cap of a mushroom-like fruiting body:-

Boletus luridiformis (*=erythropus*) Scarletina Bolete which is a reddish-brown bolete which bruises blue-black.
Leccinum roseofractum Blushing Bolete is a member of a genus with scaly stipes and interesting colour changes when cut and scraped.
Suillus granulatus Granulate Bolete has a sticky cap whose pores exude milky droplets. It is associated with conifers.
Leccinum carpini is usually associated with hornbeam.
Boletus radicans (=albidus) Rooting Bolete has yellow pores and a stalk which turns blue on bruising.
Boletus edulis is the Penny Bun.
Boletus badius Bay Bolete has a brown cap and yellowish cream pores which bruise blue-green.

The genus Amanita is an easily recognized group of mycorrhizal fungi with a ring and usually a volva:-

Amanita spissa Grey Spot Agaric has a ring, a brownish cap with a plain margin and greyish scales.
Amanita muscaria Fly Agaric is usually associated with birch.
Amanita rubescens the Blusher turns red on bruising or damage.
Amanita ceciliae Snakeskin Agaric lacks a ring and has a striate margin and flat scales. It is an uncommon species.

The Russulas are a very large genus of mycorrhizal fungi. They have caps of a wide range of pastel colours, white to orange spores, gills with or without a hot taste and some have characteristic smells. Accurate identification is now much easier with the help of a new key by Geoffrey Kibby. The park contains many of this genus still awaiting correct identification. So far I have identified the following species:-

Russula sanguinaria Bloody Brittlegill with a red cap and a pink flushed stipe. It has a hot taste and is associated with conifers.
Russula atropurpurea Purple Brittlegill is a very common blackish-purple species.
Russula ochroleuca Common Brittlegill is an equally common yellow species.
Russula xerampelina Crab Brittlegill has a smell of crabs.
Russula maculata var *bresadolana* often has a smell of cederwood pencils.

Similar to the Russulas are the milkcaps in the genus Lactarius. These produce a latex which may be mild or hot to the taste. The following milkcaps have been identified in the park:-

Lactarius turpis Ugly Milkcap has an olivaceous cap and a very hot burning taste.
Lactarius quieticolor has orange milk which turns red fairly quickly.
Lactarius quietus Oak Milkcap has a characteristic oily smell said to resemble bed bugs.
Lactarius blennius Beech Milkcap has a slimy cap and tastes extremely hot.

Another genus of mycorrhizal fungi contains the deceivers:-

Laccaria amethystina Amethyst Deceiver has a very characteristic colour.
*Laccaria laccata Deceiver has a very variable appearance.

The mycorrhizal genus Hebeloma produces rusty spores and often smells of radishes:-

Hebeloma sinapizans Bitter Pie is one of the poisonous species.

Other poisonous mycorrhizal species are in the genus Inocybe:-

Inocybe margaritispora is a rare fungus associated with hazel.
Inocybe flocculosa Fleecy Fibrecap is also an unusual species.
Inocybe geophylla var *lilacina* Lilac Fibrecap is identified by its colour.

One remaining genus of mycorrhizal fungi has been recorded in the park:-

**Paxillus involutus* Brown Roll-rim has the rim of its cap inrolled.

The mown lawns in the formal gardens are of interest as they have probably been mown for over a century; fallen leaves have been removed,and no nitrogenous fertilizers, herbicides or fungicides have been applied. Such unimproved grasslands are rare in Essex mostly confined to churchyards and cemeteries, and continuing management in the same manner is important for the conservation of the fungus flora, the most important of which is the waxcaps. The following eight species of waxcaps have so far been identified in the lawns making it a site of local importance for them, and one that should be conserved and monitored for further species:-

Hygrocybe chlorophana Golden Waxcap is a yellow species.
Hygrocybe coccinea Scarlet Waxcap is a scarlet one.
Hygrocybe conica Blackening Waxcap has a conical cap and turns black on handling or with age.
Hygrocybe fornicata Earthy Waxcap is a greyish-brownish white colour.
Hygrocybe insipida Spangle Waxcap is a smaller yellow species often with top of the stalk orange.
Hygrocybe persistens Persistent Waxcap has a yellow, conical cap, which does not turn black.
Hygrocybe psittacina Parrot Waxcap is very viscid and is unusually green in colour.
Hygrocybe virginea Snowy Waxcap is a milky-white colour.

Other species found in these lawns include:-

Clavulinopsis corniculata Meadow Coral has yellow, dichotomously branched spindles.
Clavulinopsis fusiformis Golden Spindles is larger and unbranched.
Cystoderma amianthinum Earthy Parasol has a ring on its mealy, granular stem.
Entoloma conferendum Star Pinkgill has uniquely shaped spores and is very common.
Galerina clavata is a small, brown fungus associated with mosses.
Lepista sordida forms large rings in the lawns.
Melanoleuca stridula belongs to a genus with rough spores which stain black in Meltzer's iodine solution.
Laccaria bicolor Bicoloured Deceiver is a mycorrhizal species with one of the trees near the lawns.
Mycena species or Bonnet Caps also occur here, which I still have to identify.

The rough grassland is large in extent and various fungi grow in this habitat including:-

Marasmius oreades Fairy Ring Parachute.
Psilocybe semilanceata Magic Mushroom which is toxic and hallucinogenic.
**Claviceps purpurea* Ergot is an ascomycete which is parasitic on grasses and causes ergotism.

Two large cup fungi have been identified:-

Peziza vesiculosa Blistered Elfcap is found on old straw bales and manure.
Aleuria aurantia Orange Peel Elfcap grows in grass or on bare soil.

The remaining species are saprophytic and grow on soil or in grass or amongst leaf litter. These
include:-

Coprinus comatus Shaggy Inkcap.
Coprinus picaceus Magpie Inkcap is usually found in woodland.
Macrolepiota rhacodes var *rhacodes* Wood Parasol is also a woodland species especially under
conifers.
Stropharia caerulea Blue Roundhead is a small, often greenish species with a viscid cap found in
disturbed places.
Lyophyllum decastes Clustered Bonny grows in clumps on the ground in open woodlands.
Lacrymaria lacrymabunda Weeping Widow often has droplets on its gill edges.
Lepiota cristata Stinking Parasol grows in leaf litter and has a strong unpleasant smell.
Clavinulopsis cinerioides is an unusual pinkish-grey spindle fungus.
Agaricus sylvicola Wood Mushroom is a yellowing species found on the ground in woodland.
Agaricus impudicus is an unchanging species found in woodland.
Agaricus sylvaticus Flocked Wood Mushroom turns red on cutting and usually grows under conifers.
Macrocystidia cucumis Cucumber Cap has a strong smell more like putty than cucumbers.
Melanoleuca melaleuca belongs to an easy genus to identify but the species are more difficult to be
sure of.
Clitocybe geotropa Umbonate Funnel grows in woodlands.
Clitocybe nebularis Clouded Funnel is very common.
Lepista nuda Wood Blewit is a lovely violet colour.
Lepista inversa Tawny Funnel Cap is very common.
Psathyrella tephrophylla is an under recorded member of the genus. This is probably a first record
for Essex.
**Agaricus campestris* Field Mushroom.
**Agaricus arvensis* Horse Mushroom has a better flavour.
**Agaricus xanthodermus* Yellow Stainer however can cause stomach upsets.
**Gymnopus (=Collybia) confluens* Clustered Toughshank grows in tufts or rings in leaf litter.
**Rhodocollybia (=Collybia) butyracea* Butter Toughshank also grows in leaf litter and has a greasy
cap.
**Calocybe gambosa* St George's Mushroom occurs in Spring.
**Macrolepiota procera* Parasol is probably the largest British toadstool.

The survey is as yet incomplete but already shows that Hylands Park is a rich site for fungi in
Essex. One Red Data Book species has been recorded and several uncommon ones have been
found. The lawns have proved to be a site of local importance for waxcaps and should be conserved.
Many of the specimens that I identified were collected by Mark Hanson, and additional records
were made by S. Wilkinson, and are marked with an asterisk. I have tried to use the latest scientific
names, some of which may be unfamiliar, as may be the common names, which have recently been
suggested by the British Mycological Society.

Amphibians and Reptiles

Recorders: M.W.Hanson, Pam Wilson, Peter Wilson

Records: 2000 - 2003

The commonest member of this group at Hylands would seem to be the Great Crested Newt. I have records from Home Farm, Ice-House, Pigeon, Lake Field, Ephemeral, Spring and Swan Ponds. At the latter three ponds, young have been recorded. In all probability it is even more widespread than this and would occur in many of the other ponds. I have only ever seen three Frogs in the park – one at the Writtle End and a mating pair in the small pond in the formal gardens. This pond has occasionally had spawn from garden ponds added to it. I also have only one record of the Common Toad – a single large individual found under decaying vegetable matter under the Smoke Bush in the formal gardens. The Smooth Newt has been recorded little more frequently, including in the formal gardens area.

The Common Lizard has been noted from the kitchen garden (four in number) and from the southern part of the park, five (including juveniles) were seen basking on a dead oak stump. Adders have been reported from the southern part of the park and the kitchen garden (but not as far as I am aware 2000 – 2003). Grass snakes are regularly reported, particularly and appropriately from the vicinity of the Serpentine Lake. I have also disturbed an individual basking on a fallen tree trunk in the formal gardens area.

Species Recorded

Common Frog – *Rana temporaria*

Common Toad – *Bufo bufo*

Smooth Newt – *Triturus vulgaris*

Great Crested Newt - *Triturus cristatus*

Common Lizard – *Lacerta vivipara*

Grass Snake – *Natrix natrix*

Adder – *Vipera berus*

Common Lizard

The Birds

Recorders : M.W.Hanson, the late Stan Hudgell, Graham Smith, G.Wilkinson, S.Wilkinson

Historic Records

There appears to be no historic list of birds for Hylands Park and the few records that I have come across, are widely dispersed in the literature. However, many of these are of some interest.

Like many parks in the 19th century, Hylands was part of a heavily-keepered estate. One of the earliest records is of a White-tailed Eagle shot in the park on the 11th of January 1867. The bird was set-up and displayed in the house (Glegg, 1929). Henry Corder, Honorary Secretary of the 'Sociable Grosbeaks' – a group of young naturalists (active October 1877 to January 1881) in the Chelmsford area – lived near and visited Hylands Park. In April 1878, he recorded Magpie, Chaffinch, Long-tailed Tit, Treecreepers, Field-fares, Crow, Mallard and Moorhen in the park.

In April 1879 Corder recorded that he -

"walked down to our fields near the park but only met the Keepers............... They reported hearing the Nightingale 4 days before, but no cuckoos yet. They did not consider Hawks had been unusually numerous but had shot one Merlin and Mr Pryor [Arthur Pryor – owner of Hylands] had shot a Peregrine in the Park, but it was found to be one used for Hawking purposes .... belonging to a gentleman at Chigwell [or possibly Chignell = Chignall] .... The Keepers consider Kestrels mischievous in the matter of young pheasants round a coop .... Walked through the park and found that the Goldcrests had returned ...... near a Keepers tree [gibbet] were the carcases of a Hedgehog, Weasel, Squirrel, Hen and Rabbit. On the Weasel was a fine black burying beetle".

The record is also interesting in that it confirms Red Squirrel was present at Hylands in the 19th century (the Grey did not establish itself in Essex until the 1920s). Mistle Thrush was also noted in the park.

A Ring Ouzel was seen in the park on April 14th 1878 (Christy 1890) and Peregrines were said to have been shot by the Keepers at Hylands in the autumn of 1889 (Christy, 1890). Twentieth century records for Hylands from the Essex Bird Report include Hawfinch (1969), Wood Warbler (1993), Tree Pipit (1997), Spotted Flycatcher (5 pairs) (1984) and Brambling (1999).

Hylands had a notable heronry, said to have been established when Herons nesting at Boreham House were displaced when the trees they were using were felled in 1927. The birds nested in the trees in the Ice-house Plantation (latterly also known as the Heronry Plantation). The colony contained 28 breeding pairs in 1961, but possibly as a result of human disturbance after Hylands became publicly owned in 1966, the colony declined to 15 pairs by 1970, rallied to 22 pairs in 1973, but dropped to 3 pairs in 1976 (the later summer being famously the drought year). Two pairs were reported in 1977 and none in 1978, or the following years (Cox, 1984).

The presence of Swans presumably gave Swan Pond its name and similarly a Nightingale Lane is mentioned as one of the roads closed by J.Attwood across Hylands in a road closure document dated 1843.

Birds at Hylands 2000 – 2003

A total of 86 species of bird were recorded at Hylands during the period 2000 – 2003, including those on the historic list; 92 species at least are known from the park. This figure is obviously a minimum and many more species could, with little difficulty, be added to the list – I suspect that eventually Snipe, Common Sandpiper and Sedge Warbler will be added, amongst others. It is not known how many breeding species are present in the park. I suspect the total is somewhere between 40 and 50; much work could usefully be undertaken in this area.

Of the classic parkland species, two tree-hole nesting birds are frequent at Hylands – the Jackdaw and Stock Dove. A flock of usually 50 – 70 Jackdaws were noted in late winter in the park foraging in the grasslands before taking-up nest sites in hollows, particularly in the old oaks. Stock Doves too, several pairs of which nest in the park, compete with the Jackdaws for nest sites on the old trees.

Little Owl (may have nested in 2003), Treecreeper, Nuthatch, Green Woodpecker and Great Spotted Woodpecker are other species that also utilise the old trees as nest sites. Tree Pipits were recorded, as singing males, in the southern part of the park in 1997 – 2000, but not subsequently. The Tree Pipit currently has a notably contracting breeding range in Essex and may yet be lost as a summering species in the park. Other uncommon summer visitors include Turtle Dove, Cuckoo, Nightingale (recorded as a singing male in 2001 in the Writtle Belt), Hobby (probably originating from Writtle Forest and seen 2001 and 2002), Yellow Wagtail, Garden Warbler and Lesser Whitethroat. Probably 2 – 3 pairs of Spotted Flycatchers have nested at Hylands – the formal gardens and Home Farm seem to attract breeding pairs. Goldcrests also seem to favour the formal gardens and I suspect have bred here. Common year-round residents and breeding species include Mallard, Moorhen, Wood Pigeon, Green Woodpecker, Dunnock, Robin, Blackbird, Song Thrush, Mistle Thrush, Long-tailed Tit, Great Tit, Blue Tit, Wren, Chaffinch, Goldfinch, Greenfinch, Starling, Magpie and Crow. Rooks are also frequently sighted about the park – a rookery with two nests in a tall Ash tree was started by Writtle car park in 2002 with two nests again occupied in 2003. Also in 2003 a further rookery was started in the Lower Belt (by the London Road) with five nests, possibly an overspill from the Rooks that regularly congregate in this vicinity.

Water birds are not that prominent in the Hylands list, but up to 90 Mallard have been counted in cold winter weather on the Serpentine Lake. Coot, Little Grebe and up to 11 Tufted Duck (6 male 5 female in March 01) are recorded here as well. Coot are also regularly seen on the Swan Pond. Kingfisher is also reported from here and the River Wid.

Winter visitors to the park include Siskins on Alders, Woodcock (formal gardens, South Wood, Swan Pond Plantation), Firecrest (formal gardens February 03), Grey Wagtail and small flocks of Fieldfare and Redwing. Gulls – mainly Common and to a lesser extent Black-headed – are seen on the fields in winter, sometimes over a hundred being counted.
Roman Walk attracts numbers of finches to its vicinity. I have records of Greenfinch, Goldfinch, Chaffinch and surprisingly often Bullfinches. Yellowhammers are usually also recorded here. The southern end of Roman Walk attracts numbers of Common Whitethroat.

References:

Christy, R.M. (1890) The Birds of Essex. Essex Field Club.

Cox, S. (1984) A New Guide to the Birds of Essex (EBWPS).

Glegg, W.E. (1929) A History of the Birds of Essex. London.

A Check-List of Birds recorded at (or over +) Hylands 2000 – 2003
* = recorded in formal gardens

Little Grebe
Cormorant
Grey Heron
Canada Goose
Mallard*
Tufted Duck*
Sparrowhawk*
Kestrel
Hobby
Pheasant*
Moorhen*
Coot
Golden Plover+
Lapwing+
Woodcock*
Black-headed Gull
Common Gull
Lr Black-backed Gull
Gr Black-backed Gull+
Herring Gull+
Common Tern+
Stock Dove*
Wood Pigeon*
Collared Dove*
Turtle Dove
Cuckoo
Little Owl
Tawny Owl*

Swift*
Kingfisher
Green Woodpecker*
Gt Spotted Woodpecker*
Lr Spotted Woodpecker
Skylark
Sand Martin+
Swallow*
House Martin
Tree Pipit
Meadow Pipit
Yellow Wagtail
Grey Wagtail*
Pied Wagtail*
Wren*
Dunnock*
Robin*
Nightingale
Blackbird*
Fieldfare*
Song Thrush*
Redwing*
Mistle Thrush*
Lesser Whitethroat
Whitethroat
Garden Warbler
Blackcap*
Chiffchaff*

Willow Warbler*
Goldcrest*
Firecrest*
Spotted Flycatcher*
Long-tailed Tit*
Marsh Tit*
Coal Tit*
Blue Tit*
Great Tit*
Nuthatch*
Treecreeper*
Jay*
Magpie*
Jackdaw*
Rook
Carrion Crow*
Starling*
House Sparrow
Chaffinch*
Brambling
Greenfinch*
Goldfinch*
Siskin*
Linnet*
Lesser Redpoll
Bullfinch*
Yellowhammer
Reed Bunting

Appendix species include Golden Pheasant and Feral Pigeon

Jay

Mammals

Recorders: **Alf Gudgion, M.W.Hanson, John Dobson, Sheila McDonald, Liz Appleton**

Records: 2000 - 2003

Hylands is an outstanding site for mammals in Essex. Over the recording period 2000 – 2003, 28 species were recorded. If one includes a record of Leisler's Bat found just outside the boundary of Hylands in 1995 at Chandler's Builders Merchant, then a total of 29 species of mammal have been recorded. Historically the Red Squirrel occurred at Hylands; one is mentioned on a game-keeper's gibbet in 1879, but sadly this species is now extinct in Essex. There are no records of House Mouse, but with all the utility buildings (including larders and kitchens) and a working stable block, I suspect that this species would have been recorded here.

Hedgehog

Seemingly rather infrequent. I have records from the formal gardens and road-kills on the A414 London Road.

Bats

If one admits the record of Leisler's Bat from just over the boundary of Hylands in April 1995, then seven bat species are known from the park. Brown Long-eared Bats have been found in several buildings, including the Home Farm barn and stable block. Their roosts are characterised by piles of Noctuid moth wings (at Hylands including Silver Y, Large Yellow Underwing and Copper Underwing, plus a single set of wings from an Old Lady Moth). This species was recorded in 2001 and 2002.

A late evening field visit in July 2002 in the vicinity of the Serpentine Lake and the formal gardens produced records of Daubenton's Bat and both species of Pipistrelle (*Pipistrellus pipistrellus* and *P. pygmaeus*) separated by their echo-locating frequencies at 46 kHz and 55 kHz. All three species were recorded in the vicinity of the Serpentine Lake. *P. pygmaeus* has also been recorded from Roman Walk and in the formal gardens. The large Noctule was recorded from Hylands in May 1991 and was also noted in 2002. Serotine, another large bat, was noted in the Writtle Belt and Writtle Drive area in May 1985 and here again in July 2001.

Small Mammals

A small mammal survey was undertaken in the park in October 2002. Thirty Longworth and two Jayne, Jar type flap traps were used to sample the small mammal population in the Home Farm and overgrown Kitchen Garden. The survey over two days involved inspecting the traps once in the morning and again in the evening. From 128 traps set, 64 small mammals were recorded. As is usual, it is obvious the same small mammal was re-captured occasionally, but the session produced Wood Mouse (25) Bank Vole (21) and Yellow-necked Mouse (8). These three species were common to both sites, but the Kitchen Garden also produced records of Common Shrew, Pygmy Shrew, Field Vole and Harvest Mouse. Interestingly Yellow-necked Mice proved to be more frequent in the well-wooded Home Farm area than Wood Mouse – the reverse being true in the Kitchen Garden. Yellow-necked mice are sometimes recorded in the stable block in autumn.

Rabbit and Hare

The Rabbit from anecdotal evidence (and from the amount of rabbit-proof fencing around some of the 1970s plantations – ie Home Farm and Pond) was much more abundant in the recent past. Today rabbits are controlled throughout the park, but are still frequently sighted. There is still a small, active warren in the formal gardens area. I have seen a single black rabbit in the park. Myxomatosis is also probably present. An individual with characteristic symptoms of the disease was seen near the main gate in June 2002.

The Brown Hare was apparently much more common and a breeding species at Hylands twenty years ago. It is rare now with just two sightings – one on the Lake Field in late 1999 and another disturbed from Oak Plantation in April 2003. It is surmised that human disturbance and dogs chasing the adults has caused Hylands to become less suitable. There are a number of records from fields west of the park.

Grey Squirrel

The Grey Squirrel is present and particularly noticeable in the formal gardens area. Here it will eat the newly opened buds off the Horse Chestnut trees and also raid the wheelie bins for food scraps. The species has been culled in the past, but is currently not considered to be a serious problem, Hylands being regarded as an amenity rather than a commercial forestry undertaking.

Mole

The Mole is a common species at Hylands. Some areas of the park, such as the lower Lake Field, seeming to have more than their fair share of mole hills. The mole hills that have appeared over winter have to be harrowed-out before grass mowing can begin. Moles are controlled in the formal gardens, but it is thought the burgeoning park population soon supplies another individual to take over the vacant territory.

Common Rat

The Common Rat (or Brown Rat) has been seen in a number of places in the park – formal gardens (by the lake), house, stable block, Writtle Wood, near Writtle Gate and Home Farm Pond. All sightings are of individuals; it has never been seen in numbers.

Fox

Surprisingly often seen during the day and from the evidence of 'scats', is widespread and probably common in the park. I have, however, only ever found one earth.

Mustelids

Weasels are not uncommon in the park. I made a number of sightings of individuals hunting small mammals in the vicinity of the flower beds in the formal gardens. I have seen a few out in the wider park. Stoats may have been more frequent at Hylands in the past, but I have only a record of a single individual seen running from the formal gardens to the Home Farm in March 2002.

Badgers are reported from the Park and its vicinity - sadly often as road-kills on the A414 London Road and Writtle by-pass. The re-incorporation of farmland in the north of the park with the River Wid flowing through it, has enabled the Otter to be placed on the park's mammal list. Otter spraints, with their distinctive smell and incorporated fish remains (scales and bones), were recorded 1998 – 2003 on the concrete area beneath the River Wid road bridge (Writtle by-pass).

Dormouse

Nests were recorded in 2002 in the western part of the park and near the south-east corner, a new site for this rare and declining species in Essex.

Water Vole

Recorded from the River Wid in two places in 1991 and still present here in 2001 and 2002.

Deer

Muntjac – a small, introduced Asiatic deer – have been seen at Hylands on a number of occasions. Unlike Fallow, they are solitary and most sightings are of individuals. They are sometimes chased and injured, or even killed, by dogs in the park and there have been road casualties on the A414 London Road.

Most park visitors seem to be unaware of the fact that Hylands is sometimes home to a herd of between 90 and 100 head of fallow deer. The herd probably originates from the Writtle Forest area, accessing Hylands by its non deer-proof western boundary. Mostly they visit the park at night, but it is also possible to see them in South Wood in small numbers during the day. During the foot and mouth crisis (21/2/01 – 24/4/01) with much reduced visitor numbers and dogs kept on leads, deer were often seen in numbers during daylight hours. I counted 88 in Long Broad Field. Fallow and Muntjac are both frequent in the formal gardens area, but do relatively little damage here (they are, however, rather partial to Bergenia). None of the deer I have seen are of the 'common-coloured' variety as seen in the deer enclosure at Weald Park, but mostly they are menil (with quite a range of variation) with one or two almost black individuals

Species not yet recorded

I suspect that sooner or later Mink (*Mustela vison*) will be recorded in the park – probably on the River Wid. It is already known from the Wid near Whites Bridge on the Maldon Road near Margaretting, being recorded here in 2000. The Water Shrew (*Neomys fodiens*) should be looked for in the park, particularly near the Ice-House Pond and near the old watercress bed. Lastly, I suspect that Natterer's Bat (*Myotis nattereri*) will also prove to be present either roosting, or more probably, foraging in the park.

Reference

Dobson, J. (1999) The Mammals of Essex. Lopinga Books

A list of Mammals from Hylands Park

Hedgehog	*Erinaceus europaeus*
Mole	*Talpa talpa*
Common Shrew	*Sorex araneus*
Pygmy Shrew	*Sorex minutus*
Daubenton's Bat	*Myotis daubentonii*
Serotine	*Eptesicus serotinus*
Noctule	*Nyctalus noctula*
Leisler's Bat	*Nyctalus leisleri*
Pipistrelle	*Pipistrellus pipistrellus*
Pipistrelle	*Pipistrellus pygmaeus*
Brown Long-eared Bat	*Plecotus auritus*
Rabbit	*Oryctolagus cuniculus*
Brown Hare	*Lepus europaeus*
Grey Squirrel	*Sciurus carolinensis*
Bank Vole	*Clethrionomys glareolus*
Field Vole	*Microtus agrestis*
Water Vole	*Arvicola terrestris*
Wood Mouse	*Apodemus sylvaticus*
Yellow-necked Mouse	*Apodemus flavicollis*
Harvest Mouse	*Micromys minutus*
Common Rat	*Rattus norvegicus*
Dormouse	*Muscardinus avellanarius*
Fox	*Vulpes vulpes*
Stoat	*Mustela erminea*
Weasel	*Mustela nivalis*
Badger	*Meles meles*
Otter	*Lutra lutra*
Fallow Deer	*Dama dama*
Muntjac	*Muntiacus reevesi*

Dormouse

Location of some mammal records from Hyland Park

	Formal Gardens	Home Farm	Kitchen Garden	Park
BADGER				*
BANK VOLE	*	*	*	*
COMMON RAT	*	*		*
COMMON SHREW	*		*	*
FALLOW DEER	*	*		*
FIELD VOLE	*		*	*
FOX	*	*	*	*
GREY SQUIRREL	*	*		*
MOLE	*		*	*
MUNTJAC	*	*	*	*
RABBIT	*	*	*	*
WEASEL	*			*
WOOD MOUSE	*	*	*	*
YELLOW-NECKED MOUSE	*	*	*	*

Pests and Pathogens

M.W.Hanson

The following are just a few of the pests and diseases recorded at Hylands 2000 – 2003. Historically the earliest fungal pest recorded must be the dry-rot found in the utility buildings between the main house and stable block and which caused the ultimate demolition of the buildings. Dry-rot is caused by the fungus *Serpula lacrymans*.

The park and gardens have provided a few records of interest, among them the Tar Spot (*Rhytisma acerinum*) on Sycamores in the Ice-House Plantation. Black Spot, a Discomycete fungus (*Diplocarpon rosae*) was noted on some of the rose cultivars previously on the Rose Terrace. The Oak Mildew (*Microsphaera alphitoides*) is widespread on small scrubby oaks in the park. Dutch Elm Disease, caused by a fungus of the genus *Ophiostoma*, still infects elms in the park (in the formal gardens and elsewhere). The bark beetle *Scolytus scolytus*, which is thought to carry the spores, is known from the park.

Rhododendron bud-blast is common on Rhododendrons in the formal gardens area (in January 2003 what was presumably the same species was found on Azaleas as well). Bud-blast is caused by a Hyphomycetal fungus (*Pycnostysanus azaleae*) and is thought to be carried by the introduced North American leaf-hopper *Graphocephala fennahi*. The leaf-hopper is sometimes abundant on the Rhododendrons around the north lawn in July and August.

A rust on both wild and cultivars of the daisy (*Bellis perennis*), including the Pomponette variety, is thought to be the introduced New Zealand fungus *Puccinia distincta*.

Many of the mature trees, particularly the oaks, are parasitised by bracket fungi, perhaps the most obvious and frequent of these being the bracket fungus *Ganoderma australe* (syn. *adspersum*). Rarer brackets on oaks include *Ganoderma resinaceum* and the beautiful *Inonotus dryadeus*. *Botrytis* fungus has been noted on *Geranium* leaves, usually in wet conditions in the formal gardens.

Notable 'pest' plants in the wider park include *Impatiens glandulifera* and *Senecio jacobaea*. *Crassula helmsii* is noted from the Marconi Fishing Lake – it is to be hoped it does not spread to the park ponds. Brambles (*Rubus* sp.) can be a problem growing through the Rhododendrons where they are very difficult to control.

Insect pest species recorded include the woolly aphid (*Eriosoma lanigerum*) on apple cultivars, the hoverflies *Merodon equestris* and *Eumerus tuberculatus*, presumably on the cultivated bulbs in the formal gardens, and the wood-boring beetles *Anobium punctatum* and *Xestobium rufovillosum*.

The introduced scale insect *Pulvinaria regalis*, although forming dense colonies on trees as near as Widford, is known from only two trees in the park (a Horse Chestnut and a Maple), but so far with only one or two individuals. Rather than being a vector of diseases, it disfigures the appearance of the tree when there is a heavy infestation.

Various slugs and snails are known pest species, including the snail *Helix aspersa* (which is actually uncommon in the park) and the slug *Tadonia budapestensis*. Both these species are imported amongst pots and trays of bedding plants.

There is quite an extensive list of 'weed' plant species recorded in the formal gardens:

Aegopodium podagraria   *Papaver rhoeas*
Alopecurus myosuroides   *Papaver somnifereum*
Anagallis arvensis   *Picris echioides*
Capsella bursa pastoris   *Plantago major*
Chenopodium album   *Poa annua*
Chenopodium polyspermum   *Polygonum aviculare*
Cirsium arvense   *Poygonum persicaria*
Cirsium vulgare   *Ranunculus repens*
Conium maculatum   *Rumex crispus*
Coronopus didymus   *Sagina procumbens*
Coronopus squamatus   *Sambucus nigra*
Epilobium hirsutum   *Senecio jacobaea*
Epilobium tetragonum   *Senecio vulgaris*
Euphorbia helioscopa   *Sonchus oleraceus*
Euphorbia peplus   *Stellaria media*
Fumaria officinalis   *Thlaspi arvense*
Galium aparine   *Urtica dioica*
Lamium amplexicaule   *Urtica urens*
Lamium purpureum   *Veronica arvensis*
Lapsana communis   *Veronica chamaedrys*
Myosotis arvensis   *Veronica persica*

Within the park rabbits are controlled – the numbers being kept down to acceptable levels. At one time I suspect (from anecdotal evidence and from the amount of rabbit-proof fencing) it was a serious pest. Myxamatosis is probably present in the park; a rabbit with the symptoms of the disease was seen near the main gate.

Moles are abundant in the park and the mole-hills are harrowed-out in the spring, before grass cutting in the wider park can commence. Moles are rarely controlled in the formal gardens area. Grey Squirrels are common in the park, noticeably in the formal gardens, where they raid the rubbish bins; there have been squirrel culls in the distant past. Brown Rat is widespread, but not common in the park. Foxes are probably not uncommon. Fallow Deer and Muntjac, the former at Hylands in some numbers at night, although regarded as a 'menace' elsewhere in Essex, do not seem to cause extensive problems, although both species are recorded in the formal gardens and do eat cultivated plants (including bedding plants). Deer (it is not known which species) eat the flowering spikes of Twayblade orchids in South Wood and may affect the long-term regeneration capabilities of this and other species. Deer may possibly raid the litter bins in Writtle Car Park (at night), along with Crow, Magpie and Grey Squirrel.

Conservation Status and Biodiversity

M.W.Hanson

Hylands has had no significant nature conservation status conferred upon it. South Wood and grassland in the south of the park are recognised as county sites of importance for nature conservation (SINC). The whole park (minus the recently re-acquired fields in the north-west of the park) is listed grade II* on the English Heritage register of parks and gardens of historic interest. Unlike Hylands House (also listed grade II*) this is not a statutory designation.

To date from the Field Club survey of 2000 – 2003, a total of 59 invertebrate species of national conservation significance have been recorded here (Red Data Book or nationally notable). Of these 59, 22 have been found in the formal gardens area.

The park is also home to 14 Biodiversity Action Plan Species. The park's biodiversity is further underlined by the numbers of species recorded from each of the different groups – notably higher plants (436 species), beetles (416), flies (337), spiders (92) and mammals (29).

Some comments about the park's conservation significance have, in my opinion, been somewhat wide of the mark – one writer dismissed Hylands as a "Formal park with a recreational woodland". Another work stated that the formal gardens "……are of little ecological value".

Hylands is one of the most important wood-pasture sites in Essex, outside of the better known Epping and Hatfield Forests with a significant assemblage of saproxylic invertebrates. Although dating from c.1730 the park includes elements of much earlier landscapes. It could be argued that the woods, grasslands and venerable trees represent an average Essex agricultural landscape, as it would have appeared in the 18th century and within this landscape have survived an associated flora and fauna. This landscape has elsewhere in Essex been fragmented or obliterated by modern agricultural practises.

Essex does very well for wood-pasture sites; its forests – Epping, Hatfield and Hainault – are well-known (Epping and Hatfield may be important sites in a European context). Its parkland wildlife heritage is less well known. Hylands will never compete with nationally important sites, yet it still makes an important contribution to this biotope in Essex. It is home to at least eight invertebrate species and one fungus, which have not been recorded at any other site in Essex.

The contribution that Hylands makes to Essex nature conservation needs to be re-assessed and the significance of the flora and fauna of its historic landscape recognised.

Conservation Status of Invertebrates recorded at Hylands Park

Diptera

Acanthiophilus helianthi	N
Brachyopa insensilis	N
Callicera aurata	RDB 3
Callicera spinolae	RDB 1
Choerades marginatus	N
Criorhina asilica	N
Criorhina ranunculi	N
Didea fasciata	N
Dorycera graminum	RDB 3
Epistrophe diaphana	N
Macrocera crassicornis	N
Megamerina dolium	N
Meligramma triangulifera	N
Mycetobia pallipes	N
Myolepta dubia	N
Psilota anthracina	RDB 2
Solva marginata	N
Systenus pallipes	N
Systenus scholtzii	N
Themira gracilis	N
Volucella inanis	N

Hymenoptera

Andrena labiata	Na
Andrena varians	Nb
Dolichovespula media	Na
Dolichovespula saxonica	RDBK
Lasioglossum malachurum	Nb
Lasius brunneus	Na
Stigmus pendulus	RDBK

Odonata

Lestes dryas	RDB 2

Orthoptera

Metrioptera roesellii	Nb

Coleoptera

Agrilus laticornis	Nb
Anotylus mutator	N
Bruchus atomarius	Nb
Cercyon convexiusculus	Nb
Cercyon sternalis	Nb
Cossonus linearis	Na
Eutheia scydmaenoides	N
Ischnomera cyanea	Nb
Longitarsus parvulus	Na
Nossidium pilosellum	N
Orthoperus nigrescens	Nb
Phytoecia cylindrica	Nb
Prionocyphon serricornis	Nb
Prionychus ater	Nb
Pseudocistela ceramboides	Nb
Ptinus sexpunctatus	Nb
Scaphidema metallicum	Nb
Stenus butritensis	N
Tillus elongatus	Nb
Xantholinus angularis	Na

Lepidoptera

Parascotia fuliginaria	Nb
Sesia apiformis	Nb
Synanthedon myopaeiformis	Nb

Araneae

Marpissa muscosa	Nb
Philodromus albidus	Nb
Philodromus praedatus	Nb
Zilla diodia	Nb

Pseudoscorpiones

Allochernes wideri	RDBK

Bryozoa

Lophopis crystallina	RDB 3

Park + Formal Gardens

RDB + Notable = 59 Species

Park + Formal Gardens

RDB 1	x 1	}	
RDB 2	x 2	}	
RDB 3	x 3	}	9 RDB
RDBK	x 3	}	
Na	x 6	}	
Nb	x 23	}	50 N
N	x 21	}	

RDB + Na, Nb, N

Diptera	21
Hymenoptera	7
Coleoptera	20
Araneae	4
Odonata	1
Orthoptera	1
Lepidoptera	3
Pseudoscorpiones	1
Bryozoa	1

Formal Gardens

RDB 1	x 1	}	
RDB 2	x 1	}	3 RDB
RDB 3	x 1	}	
Na, Nb + N	x 19	}	19 N

Biodiversity Action Plan Species

Triturus cristatus – Great Crested Newt

Carduelis cannabina – Linnet*

Muscicapa striata – Spotted Flycatcher*

Pyrrhula pyrrhula – Bullfinch*

Turdus philomelos – Song Thrush*

Alauda arvensis – Skylark

Emberiza schoeniclus – Reed Bunting

Lepus europaeus – Brown Hare

Pipistrellus pipistrellus – Pipistrelle*

Lutra lutra - Otter

Muscardinus avellanarius - Dormouse

Arvicola terrestris – Water Vole

Callicera spinolae – Golden Hoverfly*

Lophopis crystallina - Bryozoan

BAP Species

Park 14 Species

*Formal Gardens 6 Species

Taxa New to Essex

Invertebrates

Atomaria turgida (Coleoptera : Cryptophagidae)

Callicera spinolae (Diptera : Syrphidae)

Cossonus linearis (Coleoptera : Curculionidae)

Criorhina ranunculi (Diptera : Syrphidae)

Cylindroiulus parisiorum (Diplopoda : Iulidae)

Gyrophaena bihamata (Coleoptera : Staphylinidae)

Lophopis crystallina (Bryozoa)

Orthoperus nigrescens (Coleoptera : Corylophidae)

Themira gracilis (Diptera : Sepsidae)

Fungus

Psathyrella tephrophylla (Agaricales : Coprinaceae)

Biodiversity : Number of species recorded by order

Hydrozoa	2	Odonata	18	Pisces	6
Tricladida	2	Hemiptera	32	Amphibia	4
Bryozoa	1	Trichoptera	3	Reptilia	3
Mollusca	47	Lepidoptera	128	Aves	86
Hirudinea	5	Coleoptera	416	Mammalia	29
Isopoda	6	Hymenoptera: aculeata	72	Vascular plants	436
Malacostraca	4	Diptera	337	Bryophytes	83
Chilopoda	5	Araneae	92	Fungi	133
Diplopoda	6	Opiliones	6	Lichens	61
Ephemeroptera	2	Pseudoscorpiones	2		

Vertebrates 128, Plants 713, Invertebrates 1186. Total Species Recorded 2027.

Biodiversity

Hylands has a good range of habitats within the broad framework of a lowland wood-pasture site and a healthy diversity of plant and animal species. During the course of this work, it has become obvious that some parts of the park have a significantly greater biodiversity than others. The most important of these is the area centred on TL 677043, just east of South Wood. The habitats in this area include coppiced woodland (with areas of Ash, Elm and Hornbeam coppice stools), scrub (mature), scrub (developing), secondary woodland, plantations, green lane, adjacent agricultural land (field margins), flower rich meadow, calcareous grassland, various ponds and water course and hedgerow (Roman Walk). The whole area is well supplied with various types of dead wood and a few mature trees in grassland, plus the remaining trees from an old orchard.

Key species for this area include:

Sorbus torminalis	*Conopodium majus*	*Fissidens bryoides*
Polystichum setiferum	*Primula vulgaris*	*Ulota bruchii*
Epipactis purpurata	*Primula veris*	*Brachypalpoides lentus*
Iris foetidissima	*Agrimonia eupatoria*	*Criorhina asilica*
Listera ovata	*Trifolium ochroleucon*	*Criorhina berberina*
Daphne laureola	*Cirsium palustre*	*Choerades marginatus*
Stachys betonica	*Oenanthe aquatica*	*Myolepta dubia*
Briza media	*Ophrys apifera*	*Muscardinus avellanarius*

Other biodiversity 'hotspots' in the park would include the formal gardens and the eastern end of the Lower Belt. The formal gardens, as mentioned elsewhere in this section, are notable for their concentration of saproxylic flies and beetles.

Enhancing Biodiversity

Three projects that could fairly easily be undertaken in the park would be

1). To create a small area of arable land, just one or two acres in the north part of the park (until recently cultivated) and grow some of the now rare cornfield weeds such as Corn Marigold, Cornflower, Shepherd's Needle and Field Poppy. At the same time a seed-producing crop favourable to winter flocks of finches could be grown.

2). To recreate the flora of the former flood meadows of Widford and Surry Meads, a potential habitat for now rare plants such as Meadow Saxifrage.

3). To extend the remains of the old orchard near South Wood (traditional orchards have greatly declined in Essex) perhaps growing local varieties such as the apple D'Arcy Spice.

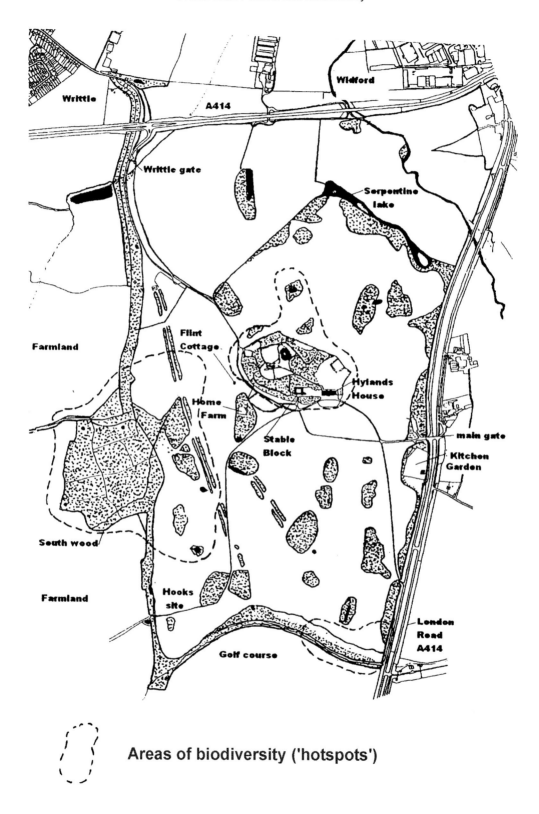

Areas of biodiversity ('hotspots')

Points of Conservation Significance at Hylands

- Good range of habitats within the wood-pasture, including ancient woodland, calcareous to acid grassland, good numbers of veteran trees, still and running fresh water and good quantity of dead-wood

- Healthy biodiversity, but concentrated in some parts of the park

- Virtually no pesticides used in the wider park – ie fungicides or herbicides. Grasslands not treated with fertiliser. Some herbicides used in formal gardens – it would be helpful if fungicides or fertilisers were not considered for use on some of the older lawns

- Now that the formerly cultivated fields in the north part of the park have been reclaimed, there is no ploughing at Hylands – deep ploughing can disturb the root-plates of veteran trees and pesticides and fertilisers used on crops can also be detrimental

- The large (577 acres) compact size of Hylands is good for conservation and since a past owner (J. Attwood) closed the roads and presumably shut-off the footpaths (ie terminated all public access) the park has no problems with excessive vehicular traffic or its associated immediate pollution

- It is a working wood-pasture of sorts, with the grasslands being cut for hay and at least some grazing pressure being maintained by a herd of fallow deer

- The trees are probably some of the best managed veteran trees in Essex

- Currently very well-managed for its wildlife, much more should be made of its potential for education in the sphere of conservation management of historic park landscapes

- Only moderate human disturbance for most of the year

- Fifty-nine Red Book Data Book or nationally notable species recorded from the park

- Home to some 150+ species of saproxylic invertebrates

- Fourteen Biodiversity Action Plan species recorded

Essex Parks – The Eulogy

In section II I have emphasised the importance of Hylands Park as a site for veteran trees and saproxylic invertebrates. Hylands is the only parkland site in Essex to have been so extensively studied. It differs from many other parks such as Weald and Danbury in being 18th century in origin, rather than medieval. As a rule of thumb, early parks should have a greater diversity of the rarer invertebrates associated with their ancient trees.

Very little work has been undertaken on the flora and fauna of Essex Parks and those that have been studied tend to be those open to the public – Weald, Thorndon and Dagnam for example. There are many parks in Essex, both public and private, that still have a recognisable wood-pasture landscape and of the parks that I have knowledge of, the following would almost certainly have significant assemblages of the rarer saproxylic invertebrates. Most of these also have good numbers of very sizeable veteran trees.

Barrington Hall (Private)	Quendon (Private)
Braxted (Private)	Stansted Hall (Private)
Dagnam (Public)	St Osyth (Private)
Danbury (Public)	Terling (Private)
Hylands (Public)	Thorndon (N & S) (Public)
Lexden (Public)	Weald (Public)
Mistley (Public)	Wivenhoe (Essex University)

These fourteen parks I suggest would be in an Essex parks premiership league from the point of view of ancient trees and probably rare flies and beetles. Some, such as Hylands and Stansted Hall, also have notable assemblages of introduced tree species.

Many parks I have visited have a recognisable wood-pasture aspect – in some this is extensive, covering virtually the whole park. In others, such as Littley Park near Hartford End, only a tiny fragment remains, but even these parks make some sort of contribution to the total acreage of lowland wood-pasture in Essex. As I have already mentioned, the estimated 4,000 odd acres of lowland wood-pasture contributed by parks in Essex may be significant in a national or even European context. Essex parks have many other important attributes beyond their wildlife.

The history of Essex parks is also in part the history of Essex. Sooner or later the name of one or other of the great "movers and shakers" in history crops-up associated with this park or that park. The great houses, sometimes built serially in a particular park are an important part of our cultural heritage, as much for the owner who commissioned them, as the architect who designed them and the usually unnamed craftsmen who built them. Their contents – furniture, paintings, statuary and libraries (as at Audley End, Ingatestone Hall and Langleys) are also of some note.

The remaining built environment of parks is also significant – the stable blocks, home farms, dairies, gate lodges, gate houses, kitchen gardens and other utility buildings, right down to ice-houses and dove-cotes and even their brick perimeter walls make a substantial contribution to the register of listed buildings in Essex.

Essex should make much more of its park landscapers. They do not come much more famous than Lancelot Brown or Humphry Repton and Repton, although born in Bury St Edmunds, lived-out his working life as a landscape gardener from Hare Street near Romford. Their influence on Essex parks in the 18th and early 19th century is still the topic of much heated debate today. The contribution of designers and architects, including Robert Adam, to landscapes such as the grade 1 listed Audley End is also important.

Public parks from the huge Hylands at 577 acres to tiny Lexden at 18.5 acres are important for the informal recreational facilities they offer. The large parks of Weald and Thorndon (combined acreage 860 acres) collectively hosted a million+ (non-paying!) visitors over the last year.

Essex parks are an astonishing legacy from the often distant past. They can, as at Hylands, be a supremely beautiful tree'd landscape, as well as an important wildlife site. They are a much-loved and enduring landscape feature – it still amuses me to see the names Crondon Park, Littley Park, Absol Park and Havering Park on modern Ordnance Survey Maps – all these parks disappeared prior to or during the 18th century – Havering went in 1652, but 350 years later it still features on a map!

Essex parks are an enduring legacy and their owners, both public and private, should be thanked for the substantial contribution their parks make to the historic and nature conservation fabric of Essex. Parks are expensive to run and maintain – I note no-one seemed to complain when the London Borough of Redbridge spent some £22,500 doing remedial work to the grade II listed gate piers of the former Wanstead House in 2003!

Recording and Registering Essex Parks

During the course of my work surveying the parks of Essex, it has become clear that our parkland heritage (from an historic and wildlife point of view) is an important, yet vastly under-rated and seemingly little-known aspect of the county's history. I would suggest that a new register of Essex parks is established, not for example in the English Heritage mould, but one that embraces all aspects of a park's identity. By that, I mean that the government bodies mainly responsible – English Heritage and English Nature - collaborate to produce an integrated register which would cover the following categories for each individual park:

Ownership

Location

History of the site – including recent maps, ie Ordnance Survey + historic estate maps + Chapman & Andre, etc

House – English Heritage status, some history, ownership, architect(s), interior designers, images (current and historic)

Park and Garden – English Heritage status, some history, landscaper(s), images (historic and current), garden buildings (and designers)

Other Buildings and Structures – status, some history (including those demolished if deemed relevant) and architects. Buildings in this section would include stable blocks, home farms, dairies, gate lodges, ice-houses, park walls, ha-has, or any other utility buildings

Details of important collections

Details of important libraries

Works of Art (statuary and fine paintings)

Fine Furniture

Nature Conservation Status

Red Data Book and Nationally Notable Species

Biodiversity Action Plan Species

Essex Red Data List Species

Brief Description of Habitats

Notable Trees –   1) Native
                          2) Introduced

References – Books, Journals, Estate Maps, English Heritage (National Monuments Record), English Nature surveys, Essex Field Club surveys, etc.

I suspect it would be viable to trial Essex for such a venture which on successful completion, could be applied to other counties in England.

The Future

A recent edition of the Essex Chronicle featured an article about a competition sponsored by the East of England Development Agency to generate ideas for a "Landmark East" - a landmark that would represent the East of England to the rest of the world. My idea would be an East Anglian Park heritage centre – a centre that brought all the disparate threads of parkland history in the region under one roof – from the history of kitchen gardens, to veteran trees, to the great landscapers, to fine Georgian furniture, to saproxylic invertebrates, to garden buildings and statuary – in fact, a celebration of all that is best about the contribution that parks, both public and private, have made to East Anglian cultural and wildlife heritage. The centre would host conferences, study days, exhibitions and provide research facilities.

Importantly, this newly-designed centre would be sited in a new parkland setting designed for people and wildlife. In essence, it would be a park designed in the 21st century with the beckoning 22nd in mind. With the history of Essex parks as outlined in this book, I would expect any such venture to be housed in Essex!

Acknowledgements

Firstly I would like to thank Del Smith for typing out the index and all the Essex Field Club Recorders and members who have contributed their expertise to the publication of this book. Their names are listed at the head of each chapter. I would also like to thank – Irene Buchan, David Bloomfield, Barbara Chapman, Robin Cottrill, CPL Aromas (Barrington Hall), Simon Damant (Wimpole Hall), Jonathon Jukes (Marks Hall), Chris Gibson (English Nature), Brian Goodey, Nick Green, Martin Gregory, Colin Jarvis, Danielle Monk, Paul Monk, Richard Morris, Roger Payne, Francis Potter, Dr. Graham Rotheray, David Sheppard, Graham Smith, Mary Smith, Sue Ward, Charles and Shirley Watson.

Special thanks must go to Chelmsford Borough Council for granting permission to record Hylands Park – Joe Cook and John Smee (without whom this book would never have happened!); the ever-helpful staff of the Essex Record Office; Prof. Oliver Rackham for his many useful comments; Alec Bull for travelling all the way from Norfolk to record the Rubi; Sue Court for putting-up with my frequent alterations to the draft book; the park owners who allowed permission for me to measure their trees and Peter Harvey, without whose editorial and technical skills this book would not have appeared.

I would also like to thank Essex County Council, The Corporation of London, English Heritage and the many local authorities and private owners who are such able custodians of our parkland heritage.

Lastly, it greatly saddens me and is very much to my regret that Stan Hudgell never saw the publication of this book. After a long and painful illness, bravely borne, Stan died on the 28th of February 2003. He made a significant contribution to the invertebrate and bird recording at Hylands and on our all too few forays to the park, his company was a great pleasure.

INDEX

A
Adam,Robert 6,31
Ashdown Forest 29

B
Barking Park (Suffolk) 29
Birds **48-52**,127,**152-154**
Boundaries 14
Bream 31
Brick-making 33

C
Cambell, Colen 5
Carp 32
Castles,
      Hadleigh 4
      Rayleigh 33
Cattle 33,36,37,38
Chalkney Wood 17,37
Chancellor and Son 34
Chatsworth (Derbs) 31
Childerditch Common 5,19
Church (in park) 34
Civil War 5
Clarendon Park (Wilts) 30
County Maps 19

D
Decoys 33
Deer 33,36,37,38
Deer-Shelter 33
Dissolution 4,17
Dove-cote 33

E
Earthworks 35
Estate Maps (E.R.O.) 24-25
Evelyn, John 5
Extent of Parks **29**

F
Falcons 33
Farm
      Model 33
      Home 34
Fences 16
Fish Ponds 31-33

Forests 54

G
Glossary **58-60**
Goats 38
Great Oaks **39-45**

H
Ha Ha 34, 129
Hawking 33
Hedges 15
Horses 37
Houses 9
Hunting Tower 31

Hylands Park

Section I 2,6,15,16,23,32,33,34,43,53,54
Section II 63-167
Acari 123
Amphibia 126,**151**
Ancient Woodland 81,132-133
Ants 118
Arachnida Checklist & Conservation
      Status 120-122
Araneae **120-122**
Avenues, Trees 71
Atkinson, William 67
Bees 119
Beetles **95-106**
Belts, Tree 71
Biodiversity **165-166**
Birds
      Aquatic 127
      General **152-154**
      Checklist 154
Brambles **142**
Bryophytes **143**
Bryozoa 125
Butterflies 124
Callicera spinolae 63,83,84,85,86,90,113,
      116,117,**128**
Centipedes 123
Chilopoda 123
Coleoptera **95-106**
      Checklist 97-106
      Freshwater 125

Conservation significance, points of **167**
Conservation status 63,85,87-94,96,97-
    106,107-109,116,117,118-119,120-
    122,128- 131,149,150,**161-166,167**
Crickets 124
Crustacea,
    Isopoda 123
    Malacostraca 125
Cultivated Landscape **70-76**
Damselflies 126
Dead Wood 115
Diplopoda 123
Diptera **83-94**
    On Ivy 86
    Checklist 87-94
    Gall causing 123-124
    Freshwater 126
Dormouse **130**
Dutrochets' Land Leech 129
Elms **139-141**
Ephemeroptera 125
Flies **83-94**
Fishes 32,126
Formal Gardens, for saproxylic species 116
Freshwater Habitat-map 82
Freshwater Life **125-127**
Fungi 146-150
Gall-causing organisms 123-124
Geology 77-78
Golden Hoverfly see Callicera spinolae
Grasshoppers 124
Grasslands
    map 80
    higher plants of 133-135
Great Crested Newt 126,**129**
Groundhoppers 124
Habitats 79
Ha Ha 34,129
Harvestmen 122
Hemiptera
    Freshwater 126
    Terrestrial 123-124
Hepaticae **143**
Hericium cirrhatum **131**
Higher Plants **132-142**
Hirudinea 125,129
History **64-68**
Hornet **130**
Hornet Clearwing **129**

House 6,23,64-65
Hydrozoa 125
Hylands-Map 69
Hymenoptera-Aculeata, Checklist and
    Conservation Status **118-119**
Hymenoptera, gall-causing 124
Ice House 33
Introduction 63
Invertebrates-Miscellaneous Checklist
    123-124
Kitchen Garden 70
Leeches 125,**129**
Lestes Dryas **128**
Liverworts **143**
Lichens **144-145**
Lutra lutra **131**
Malacostraca 125
Mammals,
    Aquatic 127
    General **155-157**
    Checklist 158
Megaloptera 126
Millipedes 123
Mollusca,
    Terrestrial 123
    Freshwater 125
Mosses 127,143
Muscardinus avellanarius **130**
Nectar Sources 115
New to Essex, Taxa **164**
Notable Dates **67-68**
Odonata 126
Opiliones 122
Orthoptera 124
Otter 131
Owners 2,64-68,70-71,152
Pale 16
Papworth,J.B. 65
Pests and Pathogens **159-160**
Pisces 32,126
Plants (Higher)
    Cultivated 75-76
    Freshwater 127
    Terrestrial **132-142**
    Noteworthy 136-137
    Weed species 160
Pleasure Garden 70
Pollard Trees 43,**109-112**
Pseudoscorpiones 122

Psilota anthracina 83,85,116,117,**128**
Pryor, Arthur 152
Reptiles 151
Repton, Humphrey 6,**11-12**,32,34,65,67, 70
Rubus fruticosus agg 142
Saproxylic Invertebrates
    Coleoptera 95-96,97-106
    Diptera 84-85,87-94
    Other Parks 117
    Veteran Trees **107-117**
Scarce Emerald Damselfly **128**
Sesia apiformis **129**
Snails and Slugs, Terrestrial 123
Snails, Freshwater 125
Soils 78
Spiders **120-122**
Standard Trees 112-114
Testacella scutulum **130**
Trees, Native 75,107-117,132,138,139- 141,144
Trichoptera 126
Tricladida 125
Triturus cristatus 126,**129**
Trocheta subviridis **129**
Vespa crabro **130**
Veteran Trees **107-117**
Walls 15,144
Wasps 118-119
Wooded Areas-Map 81
Woodlice 123
Wood-Pasture 53-54
Writtle Forest 64

I
Ingrave 29
Ice-House 33

K
Keepers Walks, Epping Forest (Map) 18

L
Lancaster Great Park (Sussex) 29
Landscapers **10**
Leez Priory 31,32
Lodges,
    Park 30-31
    Gate 34
    Queen Elizabeths' Hunting 4,31
Lyme Park (Cheshire) 31

M
Maps 17-28
    County 19
    Chapman and André 18-19,20-23,26-27
    Estate Maps (ERO) 24-25
Mews 33
Moccas Park (Herefordshire) 53
Mundon Hall 42

N
Norsey Wood 55,57

O
Orangery 34
Owners
    Attwood, John 1,15,23,65-66,71
    Audley, Sir Thomas 4
    Braybrooke, Lord (3rd, 4th & 5th) 3,31.37,38, 48
    de Burgh, Hubert 1
    Chelmsford Borough Council 63,66,68,71
    Child, Sir Josiah 5,28
    Child, Richard 28
    Church Commissioners 39
    Comyns, John (I, II & III) 61,64,66-67
    Conyers John (I & II) 7,38   Crown 1,3,4,5,13,14,31
    Essex University 40
    Gates, Sir John 1,2
    Gooch, Sir Daniel Fulthorpe 66,67,70
    Griffin Griffin, Sir John 6
    de Gynges, Reginald 29
    Hanbury, Christine 66,68
    Heneage, Thomas 7
    Hoare, Hugh 39
    Howard, Thomas 4,5
    Kortright, Cornelius 38,65,66
    Labouchere, Pierre Caesar 66,70
    Morgan, Richard 11
    Neave, Sir Richard 38
    de Neville, Hugo 3
    Petre, Lord (8th) 10,22
    Petre, Sir William 33
    Phillips Price, Thomas 40
    Pryor, Arthur 37,66,67
    Rich, Lord Richard 2,4,17
    Ruggles, Thomas 32
    de Vere 17
    Waldegrave, Lord 18

Parks, Essex
  Status of 8
  Grand houses in 9
  Landscapers of 10-11
  Heritage status 13
  Royal 13
  In S.W.Essex on 1630 map 18
  Depicted on Chapman and André 20
  Estate maps 24-25
  Pollard Oak Trees in 43-45
  Notable specimen trees in 45-47
  Birds in 48-52
  Location and access 55
  Albyns 33
  Audley End 4-5,15,18,34,35,37,42
  Barrington Hall 19,39,44,176-7
  Bedfords 2,29,38,46,47
  Belhus **21**,33
  Blake hall 33,34
  Braxted 15,16,18,34,41,54
  Castle Hedingham 33
  Claybury Hall 6
  Copped Hall 4,6-7,16,17,19,46
  Crondon 29,35
  Dagnam 41,45,54
  Danbury 29,39,43,45
  Easton Lodge 7,26,179
  Fairmead 4,31
  Faulkbourne 19
  Gaynes (Upminster) 40,41,45-46,178
  Gidea 29,33
  Hadleigh 4,30
  Hallingbury 3,44,47
  Harolds 17,29
  Hassobury 54
  Hatfield 14
  Havering 2,3,6,14,29,30,31,36,37,41,42,44
  Hill Hall 6
  Hylands 2,6,15,16,**23**,32,33,34,43,53,54
  Ingatestone 17,33
  Langleys 16,18,33,54
  Lawford 47
  Lexden 35,40,45,47
  Littley 30,34,40,41,46,54
  Marks Hall 29,33,38,40,43,46
  Mistley 19,26,39,43,45
  Navestock 19,33
  New Hall 4,18,26
  Ongar 3,6,15,29,30,31
  Pleshey, Great 53
  Pond 32,33,40,44,46

Pyrgo 2
Quendon 33,38,54
Rayleigh 29,33
Riffhams 12
Rivenhall 16,18,39
Rolls Park 34
Skreens 179
St Osyth 19,34,54
Shortgrove 15,33,54
Stansted Hall 6,33,37,41,45,47,54
Terling 33,34,42
Thorndon 5,19,**22**,33,37,38,39,43,54
Thundersley 29,33
Waltham 17,31
Wanstead 6,12,**28**,180
Warlies 6,44,46
Weald 15,26,33,34,35,38,39,40,46,54,178
Wivenhoe 40,41,44
Writtle 33,39

P
Paine, James 5
Pale 14-15,30
Pillow Mound 33
Ponds 5,31-33
Pollard Trees **39-45,109-112**

R
Rabbit 33
Rackets Court (miniature) 34
Richmond Park (Surrey) 53
Ring Hill 31

S
Saltory 30
Sheep 38
Surveyors 5,**17-18**,28,65

T
Tench 32

W
Walls 15-16
Warren 33
Wild Swine 36-37
Windmill 34
Wooded Commons 5,19,54
Wood Pasture **53-54**

Z
Zebu 38

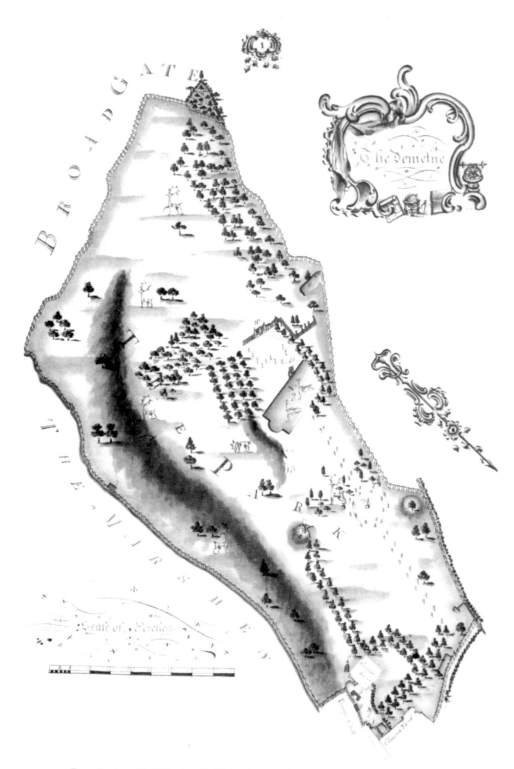

Barrington Hall Park, Hatfield Broad Oak 1766 by John Mackoun

Reproduced by permission of the Essex Record Office

Essex Parks (2004)

J. Chapman del et sculp.

Barrington Hall, Hatfield Broad Oak

Top - the hall as it appeared in c.1770 in neo-classical form. Bottom - the hall as it appeared in 1863 after extensive remodelling in the Jacobean style (Gardeners' Chronicle, 1882).

The park of Barrington Hall probably started life as the park of the medieval Hatfield Broad Oak Priory, founded in 1135 by Aubrey de Vere. The priory was dissolved in 1536 and subsequently bought by Sir Thomas Barrington in 1564, becoming the family home. The priory was apparently inadvertently demolished in the early 18th century and eventually the new hall pictured above, came to be built. The park, now in divided ownership and some disparked and farmed, still has a fine treescape including what is the largest pollard oak in Essex (girth just under 38 feet). Much of the southern part of the park still exists as a working wood-pasture with cattle grazing beneath old trees (see front cover).

The Bridge at Gaynes Park, Upminster (now Parklands)

Gaynes was originally a 106 acre park that was sold in 1929 for development. About 27 acres survive - including the bridge over the artificially widened river shown in the photograph. Neither of the two native Black Poplars to the right of the photograph now exists, but another huge specimen, girth about 14ft, survives on the very western edge of the park. It is not known who landscaped the park. (Photograph probably c. 1910).

Weald Park, Brentwood

Weald is probably the best place in Essex to get an idea of what a medieval deer park looked like, although the trees are now very much larger than would have been found then. This view is interesting, in that it shows some of the grassland that was destroyed in 1948 when a rumour (false, as it turned-out) that the ploughing subsidy was about to be lifted. (Photograph probably c.1920).

Giant oak at Easton Park, Dunmow

Easton Park was largely obliterated by the construction of a World War II American airbase. A field trip by Essex Field Club members. Pictured are J.C. Shenstone's nephew, Henry A. Cole, Raphael Meldola and Lady Warwick's agent (Photograph by J.C. Shenstone c. 1910)

Skreens, Roxwell

One of the lost mansions of Essex, Skreens was demolished c.1920. The estate had been the seat of the Bramston family since 1635. Sir John Bramston was appointed Lord Chief Justice of England in that year, the Bramston's living here until 1908. In the photograph the original house is the central block; the wings were added as late as 1911. (Photograph 1911).

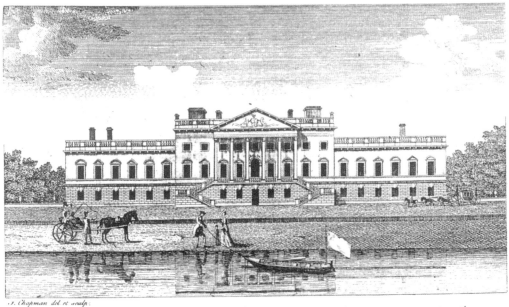

Wanſted - Houſe *the Seat of the Right Honble the Earl of Tylney.*

Wanstead House (c.1770) and a watercolour from Repton's

'Plans for the Improvement of the Grounds at Wanstead House, Essex' (1813)

Originally a 300 acre park, Wanstead is thought to have been created in 1545 as an enclosure from Epping Forest. Purchased by Sir Josiah Child in 1667, he laid out magnificent gardens and his son Richard (later Earl Tylney) commissioned the architect Colen Campbell to design the palladian mansion in 1715. The house was eventually inherited by Catherine Tylney Long in 1812 and Humphry Repton was engaged to produce suggested alterations to the grounds in 1813. The resultant watercolours, much to Repton's chagrin, were however not bound into a "Red Book" on his client's instruction (although they were later bound). Catherine's husband, the nephew of the Duke of Wellington, dissipated her fortune within ten years and Wanstead House was demolished in 1824.

Oak Pollard

Mistley Park (Furze Hills) near Manningtree in the north of the county, is home to what is probably the second largest oak in Essex with a girth of 32ft 8ins. Affectionately known as "Old Knobbly", it is just one of many notable oak pollards in Essex parks. (October 03)

The Barrington Hall Oak, Hatfield Broad Oak (Private)

This pollard oak, with a girth of 37ft 9ins (at 1.3 metres), is the largest known oak tree in Essex. I suspect it is at least 8 or 900 years old and is in remarkably good health and although hollow, has relatively little dead-wood. (November 03)

Barrington Hall, Hatfield Broad Oak (Private)

A long-established deer park with some very fine veteran trees. The park is currently in divided ownership (some disparked and farmed). The house, extensively remodelled in 1863 in the Jacobean taste, is currently a company headquarters. (November 03)

Boreham House (Private)

Built 1727 - 28 to a design probably by Henry Flitcroft for Benjamin Hoare, son of the banker Sir Richard Hoare. The park was later landscaped by Richard Woods 1771-72. Water features, such as the rectilinear canal, can be very important for aquatic wildlife. (November 03)

The Lily Pond, Dagnam Park

Park ponds can be very important for their wildlife. Many, such as the Serpentine Lake at Hylands, were created as part of a much wider landscaping scheme. The landscaper Humphry Repton liked the "glitter and sparkle" of water and he suggested that the Lily Pond - formerly in front of the now demolished house - had a chain fence "sunk" under water (hence largely out of sight), but designed to restrict the movement of cattle to a small area of the pond. (October 03)

Ash Pollard

This fine tree, a probable pollarded bundle planting at Hylands Park, has a girth of 19ft 5ins. It is also the only known site in Essex for the rare, nationally notable saproxylic beetle *Cossonus linearis*. (March 02)

The Ha-Ha at Hylands

Home to Dutrochet's Land Leech, the ha-ha also has a rich diversity of vascular plants with well over 40 grassland species being recorded. It is also the only site at Hylands for *Silaum silaus*. (June 02)

Grassland - Hylands Park, Lightfoot Garden

Grassland in the southern part of Hylands Park pictured in January and May 2001. Photograph taken from approximately the same position. Hylands has some very species-rich grasslands and around 120 species of grassland-associated vascular plants are known from the park.

Havering Park (Part public, part private)

This view, as far as the eye can see towards Hainault Forest and Lambourne End, is just a small part of what was the 1300 acre medieval Havering Park (disparked during the Commonwealth in 1652). Although its trees were known to have been sold and felled, I suspect that the apparently unploughed grasslands at this site may be survivals from the old deer park. (October 03)

Terling Park (Private)

Terling Park was in existence around 1230. These old oaks (of many) were formerly in the old deer park, but now stand in cultivated fields south-west of Terling Place. Although it is fortunate these old veterans were not felled, as is often the case, they are not prospering in their new environment.

Treescape at Hylands

Many Essex parks have outstanding treescapes, rich in native and introduced species, and many have significant assemblages of very ancient trees. Beyond that, there is an aesthetic component which is impossible to quantify and difficult to describe. In some Essex parks, such as Hylands, this quality is very evident - it is an outstandingly beautiful park, worthy of the term "pairidaeza". (November 02)

Weald Park, Brentwood

Probably the best public park in Essex to get the feel of a medieval deer park (Quendon, with its old oaks and Fallow Deer is probably a better example, but it is strictly private). Weald has grazing cattle, grassy launds, bracken and standard and pollard oak trees. (August 03)

Warlies, Upshire - House and Rotunda (Private)

This small, but splendid country mansion is a little-known treasure set in rolling countryside near Epping. The house and park probably both date from the early 18th century, but there was an earlier 16th century house on the site. Its most famous owner was Sir Thomas Fowell Buxton (1837 - 1916), the grandson of the slavery abolitionist of the same name. The park was created by Richard Morgan, who built the rotunda in 1737 and also erected the two obelisks. Morgan resided at Warlies from 1720 - 40. (August 03)

The Golden Hoverfly (*Callicera spinolae*)

This beautiful fly is the most significant invertebrate recorded at Hylands Park. Accorded Red Data Book 1 status, it is one of Britain's rarest insects, found at only a handful of sites in eastern England. Its larvae feed in rot-holes in trees. (Sept. 01)

The Blushing Bolete *Leccinum roseofractum*

Found in the formal gardens at Hylands under Birch, the Blushing Bolete is one of the *Boletus* group of fungi with pores, rather than gills. (Sept. 01)

Shelled Slug (*Testacella scutulum*). INSET. Dutrochet's Land Leech (*Trocheta subviridis*)

Two species of shelled slug (*T. scutulum* and *T. haliotidea*) have been recorded from the formal gardens at Hylands Park. Both are predators of earthworms and both species are extremely rare in Essex. (April 01) Dutrochet's Land Leech , which extends up to 9 inches long, inhabits the Ha-Ha ditch at Hylands Park. This spectacularly revolting invertebrate was discovered during the removal of accumulated leaf debris in March and April, as many as 63 specimens have been recorded here. (April 02)